DESCRIPTION OF THE COVER

Trauma had severed the relationship between the conscious and the subconscious. I built a bridge between the two using hypnosis, giving me the ability to transform irreversibly like a caterpillar into a butterfly. Now I stand emotionally, without tinnitus, having been a wheelchair user all my life. I can move between my conscious and subconscious mind because they are connected.

Table of Contents

Part C

Part D

Disclaimer

The experiences I recollect throughout this book are primarily from my time at my special needs school and other events unrelated to my family. I would like to mention that my family has given me their boundless love and support throughout my life. The adverse events that I described within these pages were beyond their control.

I have tried to recreate events, locales, and conversations from my memories of my life, my memories are imperfect, but I am sharing everything to the best of my knowledge. To maintain their anonymity and to stave off legal woes, I have changed the names of individuals and places in some instances. In addition, I may have changed some identifying characteristics and details, such as physical appearances and places of residence.

Although the author and those involved in the publication of this book have made every effort to ensure that the information in this book was correct at press time, we do not assume and hereby disclaim any liability to any part for any loss, damage, or disruption caused by errors or omissions, whether such errors or omissions result from negligence, accident, or any other cause.

"How does one become a butterfly?

You have to want to learn to fly so much that you are willing to give up

being a caterpillar." – Trina Paulus

Dedication

What vision is it when we ask strangers to build all our hopes and dreams when they do not know the truth?

I dedicate The Returning Silence to the loving memory of my mother, Mrs Kamla Ramnani (17th December 1939 - 28th December 2021), and my father, Mr Roop Ramnani. My mum and dad have been magnificent despite all my challenges and have done everything absolutely humanly possible to support and care for me. Even though I faced extraordinary challenges they have always found ways to make my life easier by often making sacrifices that some parents would be reluctant to make, which is why the reader must not assume that my childhood trauma stems from them. This is why throughout this book I have written very little about them.

I also dedicate this book to my hypnotherapist and teacher, David Corr, and my remarkable friend Phil Walder who know the truth and have helped me climb mountains. Without whom, my recovery from tinnitus would have been impossible.

Silence is not abstract; it is an entity with distinctive, recognisable qualities like tinnitus. Through my journey, I learned to make the conditions right for silence to return. The Returning Silence is my account of how silence returned to me and eventually stayed permanently.

Prologue

"To be truly radical is to make hope possible

rather than despair convincing" - Raymond Williams

About a decade ago, I had told David that I planned to write a book about my journey of recovering from tinnitus. I was a Ph.D. student and was still attending my hypnotherapy sessions. As I owed my recovery to my incredible teacher, I asked David if he could write the foreword. I had mostly won my battle with tinnitus and was on my way to full recovery. Back then, I still had the loud ringing in my ear, but it had significantly reduced in volume, and my migraines had disappeared. As soon as I submitted the first draft of my Ph.D., I had six weeks to complete the first draft of this book.

I felt honoured when David agreed to my request. Between then and now, so many things have happened in my life. My little nephew, who went to primary school, has now graduated from university, and I was Phil's Best 'Man' at his wedding. I have learned to walk one-quarter of a mile with my walker, having been a wheelchair user all my life; I have finished my Ph.D., but I also fully recovered from tinnitus, which I consider my most outstanding achievement. Hypnosis showed that the noise in my ear had meaning and purpose. However, other people's perceptions of me and my childhood trauma prevented me from recognising who I was and what I wanted in life. These erroneous

4

perceptions of myself were inaccurate but so ingrained that I started believing they originated from me. Therefore, emotional trauma needed acknowledging for closure. Over the next few years, David, through our hypnotherapy sessions, taught me how to go down to the origins of these perceptions and to dig them up from their roots. This gave me the knowledge of where these had come from and, in doing so, how they had coloured my self-perception.

Some years after beginning hypnotherapy, one evening, I bumped into a man. We are both members of the Central London Humanist Group. Over the next few years, we became very good friends. Phil became the second and final key to my incredible journey to permanent silence.

As I write this, I am aware of the silence that I hear, which is as apparent as the noise of tinnitus, as noticeable as the trains that go by a few meters away from your back garden when you first move into your new house. You hope for a wonderful and peaceful life with a new beginning that comes with a new postcode until you open the window one day and hear the loud and continuous rumble just behind your beautiful garden. Then you try to close the window, but it is stuck open permanently, or so it seems.

I wanted to write a book about living with tinnitus and how this impacted my life. However, the primary intention for writing this book about recovery from tinnitus is to provide hope for readers living with this condition.

Now in the forest tonight darkness falls like whispering sounds
upon the ground where I walk
as I walk into this forest
deeper and deeper I go
there is not a sound all around me
but I knew the forest was alive
even though I can't hear
the ending of my nerves tell me I do
I can feel it all over my body and in my mind too
and in the deepest darkest places of the forest
it's supposed to be silent at night
but it's alive with a hub of activity
but I'm not quite subtle to pick it up
so I put my ear to the ground and tried and listen carefully to what it
was saying
for there was a voice underground
it was the voice of the earth whispering to me
but not in pleasantries
it seems to be angry at me
for I have disobeyed its orders
orders of the law
indeed disabled people shouldn't roam this planet
but they do and they will
I'm not afraid of the earth anymore
and neither do I fly a flag high for disability in their scruffy clubs where
no one wants to go
I don't belong to them anymore
it was a tragedy that I was ever born in an institution made in hell
that I belong to that group of people
for I don't belong there
I knew it from a long time ago

why have you disobeyed me and stepped out of line?

I forgot to look for the reason or wait for it too

I had visions floating in my head of walking

and playing with other people my age

I would stand up alone if I wanted to

come and join us, please

they said

I said no, no way

one more step

I was falling forward into the sea of disability

where impairments were born to be proud

with their tea parties and cake

make no mistake

they had clowns too

let's talk about human rights now

I had better things to do

I couldn't stand the noise and the made-up faces

I closed the door and left them to it

there was an argument to be had one day

how can you celebrate your disability?

I would say

With their numbed-out minds and black-and-white vision

they all came from the same tragedy

my history

what does it mean to be alone in this world?

I mean truly and utterly alone with yourself

with the visions of flying free

for I'm the master of my own destiny

A Note to the Reader

Why write a book about my experience as a woman with a complex physical disability? After all, I am one of so many. Like so many others, my story may not be important, but how I achieved silence is essential. When I was growing up, prejudice and dysfunction were rife in disability services. Then again, the special needs system seemed to support others well. The problem was that the 'one size fits all' policy did not fit me. I was different as far back as I can remember. I did not identify with disability at all because I did not see the point as an individual. Just like not all white people think about their whiteness, apart from a few perhaps in the National Front, it makes sense for someone like myself not to dwell upon the fact that I am disabled. Like many children, I developed self-awareness; with this, my hopes and dreams were like those of other children. The only difference was that the imposed idea that kids like me would not amount to much moulded the thinking of, let us say, those in authority who could shape how life would turn out for me. I now have a fulfilling career I enjoy was not the life that some expected me to have. However, this book is not an autobiography of a woman with a physical disability, but an account of how trauma had robbed me of silence and the process of sorting through my trauma to find silence again.

I had written a book I wished I could have read when I experienced tinnitus and then had to listen to the unsatisfactory explanations of medical professionals related to the subject. I have a Ph.D. in an unrelated subject, have no formal background in either hypnosis or psychology, and claim not to be an expert. Therefore, this book is not the ultimate guide to recovering from tinnitus, but it will take you on a personal journey to better mental health and permanent silence. Building on my hypnotherapist David Corr's applied knowledge, I am sharing many years of personal research and experimentation into subconscious trauma, which gave me control over tinnitus and its effects.

You may have tinnitus and have no hope of recovery, are interested in hypnosis and the subconscious, or are curious to know my personal story. Throughout this book, I punctuate the writing with poetry, which may give you a more profound sense of what I was feeling. This book is not intended to be read cover to cover, so the chapter summary on the next page will help you navigate through this book to find what appeals to you the most.

Chapter Summary

The foreword to this book is written by David Corr, my hypnotherapist.

Preface: A Word on Hypnosis and Milton Erickson.
This chapter explores the limited and contorted portrayal of hypnosis in conventional media as the hypnotist reading a person's mind or making them do something against their will. Next, I introduce the pioneering approach of Milton Erickson, who defied doctors' belief that he would not live after contracting polio at seventeen (in 1918). Instead, polio heightened Erickson's powers of self-observation and reflection, which gave him insight into how the subconscious can relearn what it already knows when it might have trouble communicating to the conscious through hypnosis.

PART A: INTRODUCTION

Chapter 1: Introducing Myself
Though I was born with a physical disability, as a young woman, emotional trauma manifested as tinnitus. It almost ended my life before hypnosis provided a way out. The book's introduction includes my personal story, alongside definitions of tinnitus, hypnosis, the subconscious, and post-traumatic stress disorder.

Definitions

This section defines hypnosis, the subconscious, and the conscious.

Chapter 2: My Sound

In this chapter, I describe the effect of tinnitus, the experience of being diagnosed as irrecoverable, and my feelings of loneliness, depression, anxiety, and desperation.

Chapter 3: Having a Medical Diagnosis & the Effect of my Emotions Closing Down

This chapter highlights the pressure of being expected to act normally by those around me, which caused my regular emotions to recede, and how this impacted daily interactions.

PART B: INSIGHTS ON TRAUMA

Chapter 4: The Importance of Acknowledging my Trauma

This chapter is about finding my hypnotherapist, David Corr, and the importance of being committed to daily treatment and measuring progress towards recovery from tinnitus.

Chapter 5: The Importance of Acknowledging my Subconscious

In this chapter I explain how I dealt with the emotional backlog which had resulted in post-traumatic stress disorder and tinnitus, once hypnosis established a relationship between my conscious and subconscious.

Chapter 6: My Subconscious Expressing Itself Through the Written Word

This chapter highlights how the subconscious can express itself through the form of questioning using minimal words and removes ambiguity, allowing the person to respond from a deeper source than the conscious. I describe the concept of Clean Language and how this uses the techniques of Automatic Writing.

PART C: SUBCONSCIOUS EXPRESSION

Chapter 7: Automatic Writing and my Subconscious

This chapter outlines how to allow the subconscious to express itself through the written word. It first explains the concept of Clean Language and its use, moving on to the Automatic Writing method and then describing practical exercises. Finally, it examines the method of Focusing, where the subconscious can explore an issue and find a resolution.

Chapter 8: Automatic Writing

This chapter explains how Automatic Writing enables the subconscious to express itself without intrusion by the conscious and introduces the benefits of applying this technique.

Chapter 9: Automatic Writing Exercises

This chapter includes six Automatic Writing exercises and how they enabled me to unlock the once-hidden memories, thoughts, feelings, and emotions out of bounds to my conscious self.

Chapter 10: Focusing

This chapter introduces Eugene Gendlin's Focusing technique, which I have adapted by combining with Clean Language and Automatic Writing to assist the subconscious in revealing responses from a deep source.

PART D: DREAMS

Chapter 11: Dream Analysis

This chapter explains the importance of dreaming while illustrating the steps of dream analysis using Automatic Writing to reveal emotional messages from the subconscious.

Chapter 12: How to Improve Dreaming

In this chapter, I explain how I developed and refined methods and techniques of dreaming through trial and error until they became effective in my recovery.

Chapter 13: Writing a Personal Dream Lexicon

This chapter provides more detail about the dream analysing process remains essential even after the period of Dream Analysis has ended.

PART E: EXERCISES

Chapter 14: Practical Exercises for the Subconscious

This chapter looks at how the subconscious reveals itself through several short mental exercises, which you can do in your own time and reduce tinnitus.

Chapter 15: Burning Letters

This chapter describes how I re-engaged with two traumatic events in my childhood that needed closure, using writing to put the past to rest.

Chapter 16: Metaphor Exercises

This chapter explores how to be mindful in everything you do, encouraging the subconscious using hypnosis, and ensuring that the subconscious stays open as you carry on with daily life. This often reduces the sound of tinnitus - metaphors like fly-tipping permit this to happen through simple stories.

Chapter 17: Calming Exercises

This chapter includes additional exercises to bring a sense of calmness, often reducing tinnitus.

PART F: PRACTISING SILENCE

Chapter 18: The Home Stretch of Returning to Silence

In this chapter, I explain a new way of living, one which anchors my daily experience in emotional reality, allowing me to feel emotions that are necessary for recovery from tinnitus. I discuss the necessity of acknowledging my deepest desires and how this helped me change my lifestyle to recognise what I actually wanted at an emotional level. I was nearly there and could see the summit of the mountain. Silence was but half a yard away. However, this part of the journey left me exhausted, unfocused, and unable to concentrate. Even then, it was worth it. I explained why I found it difficult to express what I was going through to anyone. Finally, this chapter highlights examples from my life that increased my tinnitus and my coping strategies to counter the condition. I have also explained how to reduce tinnitus when emotional trigger points make tinnitus louder.

Chapter 19: Conclusion and Epilogue

This chapter reveals how my best friend was crucial to my recovery and how he helped me complete my journey. I conclude by describing the immense joy I experienced through the love and friendship that Phil and I share and how this was vital to my recovery. It is now time to move on and learn to live rather than survive. This epilogue describes a small, simple but important ceremony conducted by Phil to provide closure to one of the most challenging periods of my life and to celebrate the beginning of a new start where I experience silence permanently. I thank David Corr for helping me to gain control over my recovery by imparting his wisdom about the subconscious and how it is possible to connect and communicate with it. David saved my life and will always be my hero, and so will Phil.

Foreword

This book is a remarkable testament to its writer, Sapna Ramnani. In these pages, you will find so much to inspire you. It is, at one level, a book about therapeutic hypnosis and recovery from tinnitus. At another level, a searing critique of both the medical and social models of disability. At an even deeper level, it is a call to live with a fierce, joyful, and creative commitment to whatever challenges one faces. This book, however, will be of little interest to anyone seeking a quick fix. To be sure, remarkably rapid healing can and does occur. Oftentimes though, healing, especially the healing of deep emotional wounds, takes time, patience, and persistence – and Sapna embodies these qualities so potently.

What makes Sapna remarkable as a person and client is that she took her part in the therapeutic process seriously. She took the ideas, tools, and theoretical possibilities we explored in the sessions and made them her own. There are areas where Sapna's and my understanding of what we did and what it meant diverge, sometimes radically so. But what is not in question is Sapna's commitment to heal. If you take nothing else from this remarkable book, it is that by becoming an active participant in our own healing, extraordinary things can happen. It is an enormous honour to write this Foreword, and I commend this book to you. I advise reading it slowly and allow yourself time to deeply explore and reflect upon what is on offer.

Take whatever resonates for you and translate those ideas and techniques to align with your individual circumstances.

Enjoy the journey.

David Corr, September 2022

Invisible Sirens

The invisible sirens were still blaring when hands drew back the curtains, forcing open my eyelids. Long after midday, the noise was still there when they swung my legs over the edge of the bed and secured me into a chair. A hammer hit my head repeatedly, almost breaking my skull as if determined to penetrate my brain. My parents decided to get me up since it was nearly twenty-four hours since I had last eaten or drunk anything. My head thumped like it was still in a hellish all-night rave. However, I had not been partying, and I was not hungover. In fact, I had been to the doctor instead.

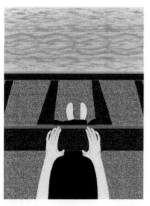 The owner of the hands and the other inhabitants of the house were unaware that I was standing on tiptoes on the edge of a bridge, trying to fight back the deafening roar pushing me off. This was not a dream or even the memory of a dream, but the constant feeling I had because of the ringing in my left ear that grew louder with each passing day. I had not slept for forty-eight hours, so I hoped I would crash out tonight because of exhaustion. The so-called expert 'audiologist' in the hospital had told me I must learn to live with it, like so many other people who had this thing, and that I did not need

to worry since he would teach me how. This thing, called tinnitus, is an unwanted sound in one or both ears, even when there is no sound in the environment. Holding on to the cold and hard edge of that bridge, I knew I had experienced many unpleasant things in life, yet I was not sure I would be able to handle this one. As the only one who could hear the noise, I was alone, even though I lived with a family who loved me beyond bounds.

Preface - A Word on Hypnosis and Milton Erickson

Hypnosis is not about someone swinging a pocket watch in front of a person trying to control their mind and making them do things they might not be fully aware of or would normally consent to. A common misconception of hypnosis is that a therapist does something to a client. Indeed, this does not help the perception of hypnotherapy. This misguided portrayal of hypnosis has damaged society's understanding of this subject. Popular historian Robin Waterfield suggests that, "...the prehistory of hypnotism in the West, in the centuries preceding Mesmer, is poorly documented and hard to excavate."[1] This could be why hypnosis is not fully understood by those who have not studied it in depth. In addition, many religions describe a trance-like state where believers become so caught up in prayer and the act of the priest that some get up and dance while others fall down when touched by the so-called 'Holy Spirit'. All these perceptions harm the authentic practice of hypnosis as one of emotional recovery. Therefore, I have purposefully avoided the term emotional healing because of its religious or paranormal connotations, which damages what Milton Erickson began to develop.

Photo courtesy of The Milton
H. Erickson Foundation, Inc.

Erickson was a leader in the field of hypnosis, and many regarded him as second to none. In the early 1950s, professionals and thinkers, including Aldous Huxley, sought his advice on hypnosis and altered states of consciousness. Erickson's childhood was not smooth sailing as he had physical difficulties. He contracted polio at seventeen and spent many years in bed. One day, Erickson overheard the doctor telling his mother that he would be dead by the next morning. This was a distressing thought for a boy on the verge of becoming a man; overhearing this infuriated Erickson, inspiring a deep desire to prove the medical profession wrong. Over the next few years, Erickson had to relearn to walk. His power of observation meant that he noticed how others normally moved, especially his baby sister, as she learned to stand and walk. Later, in his hypnotherapy sessions with his clients, Erickson would deliver a story that would describe the obvious, like the example of how to walk and the associated problems with learning to stand. This would cue the subconscious, preparing it for a new message. He would then deliver the message; by this time, the subconscious would have prepared itself to receive it. The message would activate the subconscious to acknowledge what it already knew and to utilise it in this context. This is the principle of utilisation that Erickson would later develop in his practice, one which is threaded through my own experience.

Throughout his career, Erickson reflected on how his experience with polio brought him to be a hypnotherapist, developing his theories and methods of working. He said, "We learn so much at a conscious level and then we forget what we learn and use the skill. You see, I had a terrific advantage over others. I had polio, and I was totally paralysed..."[2] He used his paralysis to hone his hypnosis techniques, turning something negative into a learning experience. As Sidney Rosen, a close friend and student of Erickson's, comments,

> "Erickson is suggesting that a disability may give one an advantage, a "terrific advantage over others." He suggests that learning is one of the best forms of entertainment. When he is completely paralysed he asks, "How can I entertain myself?" He follows that by describing how he developed his powers of observation. Then he tells about the pleasure of further learning—learning the things that are ordinarily unconscious—and gives the example of our unconscious actions and movements as we walk down the street."[3]

Michael D. Yapko is a clinical psychologist and author whose work focuses on treating depression, creating short psychotherapies, and developing clinical hypnosis applications. Yapko believes that hypnosis is a process of the subconscious relearning what it already knows but could have trouble communicating to the conscious because the conscious may not be receptive or be aware that it has a problem and that this needs a solution. Although Erickson disagreed with the common notion at the time that people with symptoms were solely pathological, he also recognised their strengths.[4]

John Grinder, Judith Delozier, and Richard Bandler, three neurolinguistic programming researchers who worked closely with Erickson, explain the role of the conscious and why it processes a limited amount of information.

> "The amount of information available from our ongoing experience greatly exceeds our ability to sense our experience consciously. In fact much of the process of learning and growing is our ability to sense regularity or pattern in our experience and to develop programs within ourselves to cope effectively with the world at the unconscious level of behaviour."[5]

For example, in reading this sentence, you would have conditioned yourself to associate every letter with a sound and then learn to combine the letters to form words that have meaning, which you also had to learn as a child. However, once learnt, it is possible to read while being undisturbed by the problem of not recognising letters. This is because the act of recognising letters and how they sound is handled subconsciously, while the conscious is preoccupied with comprehending the meaning. They explain, "...how cluttered our experience would be, for example, if it were necessary for us to consciously maintain the rate and depth of our breathing, the tones of our muscles, the level of our blood sugar..."[6] When this process goes wrong, as with tinnitus, the conscious can adopt automatic behaviours that are inappropriate for the situation, based on the need to protect itself in the moment from traumatic events. Gilligan reminds us of the inevitability of life; he says,

"... every basic experience of being human will visit you, over and over again. There is nothing you can do to avoid it: simply by virtue of being alive, you will be touched repeatedly by sadness, happiness, anger, joy, disappointment, and so forth."[7] It is necessary to embrace all the experiences that life offers because we are human with emotions that help acknowledge all that we feel. A further explanation of post-traumatic stress disorder is on p. 111. When the conscious does not function for the intended purpose, the modelling of the conscious becomes incorrect, which is why we experience ineffective suffering. However, hypnosis provided me with a solution and a journey that had a positive endpoint, a way out of torture.

In my understanding of hypnosis, instructions are turned into metaphors that are easily absorbed and acted upon at a subconscious level. Indeed, some of the hypnosis practices that I describe in this book seem, at one level, simple and similar to a game for primary school children. Erickson's approach was based on story-telling, using metaphor to provide guidance and tools to the subconscious in such an effective way that it can use them to elicit change. So, for example, as Rosen writes, "By describing plausible experiences that an infant might have in learning to stand and walk, he encourages regression of the listener to the infant level."[8] Erickson described problems in the past tense while he put solutions in the present tense, which is how this book is written. This helps the subconscious to associate problems with the past because it is impossible to alter the actual event, but it is under our control how we experience the present. Even though our history is written in stone, we have the ability to change our emotional response to what we experience, lessening the emotional hold that it has on us. The conscious, according to Erickson, is the most limited part of a person, and he emphasised, " Even though your conscious mind is very smart ... your unconscious is a lot smarter than you are..."[9] Hypnosis taught me to trust the wisdom of the subconscious, which has been hugely beneficial in the journey of my recovery. Erickson's ability to deliver an experience and invite his client to make what they want of it, even nothing at all, was the foundation of his hypnosis practice as a therapist. He invited his clients to play along with him, using their imagination in a therapeutic tale he created individually bespoke to them.

A person's emotional support system extends into a dark and invisible universe of the subconscious, one which we are only beginning to understand. This consists of dreams and subconscious thoughts that influence our lives in ways we often do not understand. These deep emotional roots are our vast underground source of knowledge and wisdom. These stories seemed unimportant and meaningless at one level, but on a deeper level, often below conscious awareness, the stories would have meaningful metaphors. Subsequently, these could be absorbed subconsciously, which helps the subconscious repair by now being given the tools in the form of metaphor. Yapko describes hypnosis as, "...a focused experience of attentional absorption that invites people to respond experientially on multiple levels to amplify and utilize their personal resources in a goal-directed fashion."[10] Erickson would learn in what contexts a client uses a particular metaphor, and he would create an experiential narrative around this metaphor that would go directly into the subconscious. Rosen further comments, "This was one of Erickson's important principles—that people have, in their own natural history, the resources to overcome the problem for which they are seeking help."[11] Infinite emotional and mental possibilities can be partly explored through metaphorical story-telling, which was Erickson's main approach. As Gilligan explains, "The principle of infinite possibilities can also be realized through metaphorical stories." [12] For Erickson, hypnosis was a living practice, and my experience is along the same lines. I was in bed one day because my tinnitus was so loud, giving me a headache.

My five-year-old nephew came bursting into my room, and we started talking. He told me a story he made up as he went along. The story was about two types of creatures, one good and one bad, and there was a conflict between the two. Eventually, the good creatures overpowered the bad by shooting beautiful colours at them using a magical gun. My nephew had created a story with a metaphorical conflict and described it vividly. He narrated the resolution with equal vividness, using colour to help me imagine the scene. When he finished telling me the story, my tinnitus had almost disappeared. This shows that sometimes it is about choosing the right metaphor to go with the right story, which will motivate the subconscious to reduce the intensity of the tinnitus.

Part A - Chapter 1

Introducing Myself

In my mid-thirties, I noticed a faint noise in my left ear. Initially, it was barely audible, but it became increasingly louder over the following months. I visited my doctor, who examined my ear and informed me that a wax buildup was the likely cause. The noise was still there when the wax was removed. My doctor referred me to an ear, nose, and throat specialist at a London hospital. Several hearing tests and examinations proved inconclusive, and in 2008, I was diagnosed with tinnitus.

"Tinnitus" is derived from Latin and means "to ring". It is very challenging to deal with, and several things could cause the condition. Towards the end of 2009, the sound gradually grew louder, and insomnia set in. I could not sleep for three or four days, after which the exhaustion meant that I slept for around fourteen hours, losing whole days. And then, another cycle of insomnia followed. By this time, the noise in my ear was unbearably loud, like a jet engine. The doctors said I would have tinnitus all my life, which would get worse with time and could not be treated. It was one of my worst times, and I contemplated suicide.

When I looked online, the only information I found was about coping strategies and how to live with tinnitus, but it seemed like I would die of this condition if it became any worse. On one December evening in 2009, I noticed David Corr's website at the top of the search engine. He was a hypnotherapist and happened to be an expert in how the subconscious works. I had never thought of hypnotherapy before and knew nothing about it or how it worked. Having seen the media's portrayal of hypnosis, I was sceptical, but I had nothing to lose, so I agreed to meet him in January 2010. I did not know it then, but David turned out to be an incredible teacher whose knowledge of applied hypnosis and tinnitus from a psychological perspective became the first small but crucial step on my long journey to permanent silence.

David taught me that when we experience emotional trauma, the resulting unacknowledged emotions are suppressed back into the subconscious or expressed consciously in a highly diluted form, resulting in emotions that are not entirely felt. It is essential to simultaneously be aware of more than one emotion to have a balanced view or emotional reaction to a situation we are experiencing. With tinnitus, the conscious became a strict gatekeeper, confining emotions and associated painful memories to my subconscious. This is one reason my conscious stopped experiencing emotional pain in the moment. Gilligan suggests that we must completely immerse in every experience it brings so that we can let it go.[13] Buddhists call this practising mindfulness or being mindful. Out of the multitude of possibilities as to why one's tinnitus could be loud, there is no way of correctly guessing. Hypnosis provided me with a way to find so many needles in so many haystacks, and when I found all of them, I experienced silence. For beneath the trauma of life is the real you fighting to break free, but life has pulled us in many directions; this is why we forget to listen to ourselves because trauma drowns out that inner voice. This book is about how to connect with that voice, to understand what it is saying to us so that the past does not come knocking at the door, and this is how we can be silent again.

I attended a special needs school from the age of five to just before my seventeenth birthday, which was a harrowing experience, as I outline in chapter three. It is easy to recollect memories of my time at the special needs school; some are highly vivid. However, from the time just before I developed tinnitus, it was impossible to bring up the emotions and feelings associated with these memories. Essentially, the bridge between the subconscious and the conscious was broken; this meant that memories, thoughts, and emotions were isolated in the subconscious. Through hypnosis, I learned that we have to move beyond all that we see to all that we feel to understand ourselves better and not be frightened of this process. This book retells how I rebuilt this bridge, brick by brick, which returned me to better mental health.

Chapter 2

Background

The traumatic experience of being born with a disability and experiencing life with an impediment manifested as tinnitus when I became a woman. It almost ended my life before hypnosis provided a way out. In this book, I have interwoven a personal story and definitions of tinnitus, hypnosis, the subconscious, and post-traumatic stress disorder.

For those who have tinnitus, recovery is rare. I imagine those with this condition can learn to live with it, but some may take their own lives if the noise becomes unbearable. I am one of those rare ones that have made a full recovery, and this book is the story of how this became possible. The motivation for writing this book was born out of the frustration and desperation I felt when I was diagnosed with tinnitus. I had almost lost hope; just when I thought there were no answers, there were so many.

In my attempt to write the first draft of this book, I hoped to put together a practical guide with scientific explanations, along with a few tweaks I made to prevailing therapeutic practice. First, I thought it would be useful to people with tinnitus. Later, both close friends and editors suggested that including my personal story for context would make the book more credible and helpful. Many people with disabilities write their life stories because they may have a burning desire to tell us their experiences, expressing their frustration with how they had been treated unfairly by the system or people around them. Some people think disability is unusual, strange, different, out of the ordinary, and a triumph over tragedy, which readers cannot resist. I do not belong to these categories; in fact, one of the things I value most is privacy. I do not talk about my childhood or disability to even my close friends, so I was reluctant to write about it. However, my experience of having a lifelong physical disability is so interconnected to my tinnitus that this book would be incomplete without recounting my personal experience. I am not a victim of my history, but I wrote this book from the perspective of a mental health survivor who recovered from tinnitus by eventually becoming my own hypnotherapist.

This book offers a personal road map of my journey, from understanding the practices and principles of hypnosis to assisting my subconscious emotions to manifest without tinnitus. This book is the culmination of many years of reading, research, self-experimentation, and learning from my hypnotherapist and teacher, David Corr, who has been influenced heavily by the unique approach of Milton Erickson and his protégé Stephen Gilligan.

Like tinnitus, silence is not abstract; it is an entity with distinctive, recognisable qualities and can be nurtured in the right conditions. The Returning Silence is my account of how emotional tranquillity returned to me and eventually stayed permanently. As this book demonstrates, my journey was personally significant, and I have completed it; unfortunately, many people still have tinnitus or emotional trauma that expresses itself in other forms.

This book, which includes a foreword by David, interweaves a literature review and a personal narrative based on the notes and journal I have kept since my first few appointments with David. While I will not describe my hypnotherapy sessions with David in detail, I use generalised examples from my life to chart the progress of my recovery and to discuss hypnosis principles and how these were put into practice during the entire process. I offer this book to those suffering from tinnitus, clinicians, psychologists, audiologists, mental health professionals, and anyone who may wish to further their knowledge of tinnitus, the subconscious, and emotional trauma with innovative approaches.

Essentially, recovery was a journey to become who I am today, by discovering who I was in the past, to transform into my true self ultimately. Before, it was as if I looked at myself in the mirror while wearing second-hand clothes others gave me. Through hypnosis, it was possible to see those second-hand clothes for what they were, who had given them to me, and how they had shaped my self-identity. Hypnosis provided the insight I needed to make this process possible. This happened partly through discovering the emotional perceptions that had originated from others. Underneath the psychological trauma of being a disabled child, this emotional trauma was hidden in my subconscious without being detected consciously. Charles R. Figley, an author who deals with 'trauma' as a subject of enquiry, suggests that in the past, trauma was thought to stem solely from injury to the body, but later, trauma was recognised to have a physical cause. It was later acknowledged that mental wounds occur during a lifetime, just like a physical injury. Trauma was understood to penetrate the mental defences of people, causing[14] the conscious to absorb the impressions and negative perceptions of others. For me, it was like having no emotional immune system because trauma had broken down the defence barrier, making me vulnerable to other people's emotions. Once I had consciously understood and acknowledged these emotions, using hypnosis to connect the subconscious with the conscious, my feelings finally found their peace, returning me to silence.

Identity

I don't know where I'm going
but I travel alone into my real identity
and into my real home
into the sunset of tomorrow's dreams
and dreams yet to come
without pollution from life itself
for I'm pure as gold and hard as rock
I have only myself to blame
some would say
but I broke the mould of yesterday to survive without strife
as I live in your world tonight

Each of us has a sense of identity that allows us to understand at a conscious level who we are to ourselves and to others. Over time, the conscious identity develops and transforms. Sally C. Prebble et al., a University of Auckland researcher, believe that whatever we understand and believe about ourselves is self-knowledge. These include likes, dislikes, personality traits, goals, values, abilities, physical attributes, and knowledge about our lives. These lay the foundation for how we see ourselves as unique individuals with distinctive personal histories.[15]

Hypnosis aids the subconscious to reconstruct a "new" identity by breaking down the identity of the conscious, which may have been constructed by the perception of others. This new identity might be the old and original identity of the subconscious, which makes it "true". Hypnosis encouraged me to search for my old and original identity that trauma had buried entirely. Hypnosis had set alight something in me. I was returning to an older landscape, something that felt more alive. My subconscious was in recovery as it was releasing its emotional baggage through the conscious. To return to my original identity as Sophia, the female subconscious part of me, I needed to find my original roots, bypassing the trauma and the negative perception of others. I then discovered the multiplicity and depth of my emotional self. Hypnosis provided a link to myself at a deeper level, one that was instinctive, emotionally more profound, and richer, and one that allowed me to recognise the whole of myself. This new identity felt unfamiliar and uncomfortable to the conscious; it was like wearing a suit when I had never worn one before. It fitted well, and the mirror said it was perfect. I looked smart, but felt uncomfortable because it was not what I was used to; this is how my subconscious and conscious connected.

It took me some time to become accustomed to my original identity, but through Automatic Writing, my subconscious constantly reassured me. The person I am now was who I was meant to be before the trauma of life, and the impressions of others severed the connection between my consciousness and the subconscious. Silence returned when this link was re-established between the two and once my trauma was examined and dealt with at a conscious level.

After a few initial appointments with David Corr, I found slight improvements in noise reduction. In addition, my once permanent migraine had disappeared after my first appointment, and I was sleeping again. With David, I saw that recovery was possible, which gave me the confidence and the motivation to overturn the medical prognosis. A few weeks later, I went back to the 'audiologist' and smiled as I told him I was on my way to making a full recovery and that I never wanted to see him again. It was a beautiful sunny day when I stepped out of the ENT hospital in London. I went for a bite to eat while feeling overwhelming relief that my journey towards permanent silence had already begun.

Some Statistics on the Population with Tinnitus

According to the British Tinnitus Association, approximately thirty percent of the population will eventually have tinnitus in the UK. However, roughly thirteen percent of adults (one in eight) have persistent tinnitus.[16] While the American Tinnitus Association suggests that 25 million Americans suffer from it, which makes up ten percent of the adult population.[17]

The following statistics are the global sample population with tinnitus which were reported in the Lancet Regional Health, Europe in 2022:

Among 11,427 participants (5404 men and 6023 women) aged 18 to 99 years (participants' age was 18 to 64 in Greece, and 18 to 74 years in Latvia), 14·7% reported any tinnitus (14·0% men and 15·2% women), 6·0% reported bothersome tinnitus (5·0% men and 6·6% women), and 1·2% reported severe tinnitus (1·0% men and 1·4% women) ... The prevalence estimates for any tinnitus ranged from 8·7% in Ireland to 28·3% in Bulgaria, for bothersome tinnitus from 3·4% in Ireland to 11·5% in Bulgaria, and for severe tinnitus from 0·6% in Ireland to 4·2% in Romania... The category of severe tinnitus in each country had small sample sizes ranging from seven individuals with severe tinnitus in Ireland to 35 individuals in Romania. The only statistically reliable pattern by geographical region was that Western European countries had significantly lower odds of any tinnitus compared to Northern European countries (OR was 0·69; 95% CI: 0·520·92).[18]

These statistics do not differentiate between tinnitus which has a physical cause (damage to the inner ear) and tinnitus due to psychological reasons. Typically, people with tinnitus may also experience hyperacusis or decreased sound tolerance, misophonia, which is the intense dislike of sound, or phonophobia which is the fear of sound.[19]

I experienced all three while suffering from tinnitus. I could not tolerate the sound of the vacuum cleaner or the sound of a police siren. These types of sounds would not only increase my tinnitus but also would put my nerves on edge. These sounds affected me the same way some people react to nails being scratched against a blackboard. Tinnitus can be the result of physical damage to the inner ear or the result of an unrelated psychological trauma. There is a correlation between the experience of psychological trauma and the onset of tinnitus, but a clear causative relationship is an open question[20]. For medical professionals to provide appropriate treatments, psychological tinnitus should be viewed as a manifestation of post-traumatic stress disorder (PTSD). This book concerns psychological trauma as a cause of tinnitus, which very few medical health professionals recognise and are unequipped to deal with. In my experience, even though the research into tinnitus treatment provides a foundation for the successful understanding and recovery from tinnitus, it demonstrates a lack of consideration for this condition's emotional and psychological dimensions.

While examining existing medical research on tinnitus, I discovered that the medical community has limited understanding, and therefore, their reticence resulted in poor outcomes for those living with tinnitus. A study by Professor Pawel Jastreboff of Emory University, Atlanta, suggests that,

> "...overstimulation of the sympathetic autonomic system [sympathetic autonomic nervous system controls bodily functions, e.g. heart rate, blood pressure, and response to stressors or trauma] by any means results in the same negative reactions as reported by tinnitus patients, e.g., annoyance, anxiety, panic, problems with concentration, decreased ability to enjoy activities in life, sleep difficulties, depression, impaired concentration, and irritability."[21]

While Jastreboff accurately describes these symptoms and successfully recognises the link between tinnitus and the subconscious, the study further explains a possible treatment for tinnitus[22] is that, "...habituation of negative reactions to tinnitus and habituation of tinnitus perception..." and "...extinction of subconscious conditioned reflexes connecting the auditory system with the limbic and autonomic nervous systems."[23]

This may reduce the perception of tinnitus but fails to address the fundamental cause. By blocking the subconscious path, it becomes impossible for the subconscious to communicate with the conscious and for the conscious to realise that something is wrong. The subconscious may try other ways to get your attention if the path of communication is blocked; this may cause tinnitus or other symptoms. Therefore, it becomes essential to hear the volume of tinnitus to gauge recovery (see p. 123 of this book). Thus, Jastreboff acknowledges that "...even when patients are not aware of the presence of tinnitus, they can still be negatively affected by it."[24]

Temporary Relief By Listening To Another Sound

Listening to another sound may give some momentary relief to the experience of tinnitus, and there are several recommended ways. Total masking is when white noise cancels out the sound of tinnitus, providing temporary relief, and this is what I listened to when I first had tinnitus. Partial masking is when white noise is played to distract from the sound of tinnitus. Alternatively, sound therapy is where music is in the background as a pleasant and distracting sound to counteract the sound of tinnitus. Professionals, such as audiologists and general practitioners, frequently recommend one. While these have momentary benefits, they do not address the underline cause of tinnitus. Having read some of the literature aimed at professionals and those with tinnitus, I was surprised that hardly any of it focused on recovery and cause. As these approaches are flawed or aimed at temporary relief, I have attempted to explain tinnitus and recovery using the lens of hypnosis and the subconscious.

A Necessary Ball And Chain

I needed to have white noise constantly playing in the background to reduce the tinnitus and maintain it there. Before I began hypnotherapy, this was the only recommendation made by my doctor. The white noise CD would constantly play, especially at night; without it, I could not sleep. Effectively, it was like having a ball and chain, but one which would lessen the noise temporarily, and I wondered if this would be my life. During the first few months of hypnotherapy, David asked me to undertake specific hypnosis exercises daily when I hardly knew anything about this subject. As a result, I became more aware of the type of sound I heard and how it changed. Sometimes, I would listen to a different sound in each ear or just in the left ear. There were other times when I tried to visualise the sound as an image to be able to manipulate it, as I had learned through hypnosis. However, often I could not think of a mental image that fitted the sound exactly. It felt as if the sound was trying to outsmart me by finding a way to force me to listen to it, and that is why I perceived it as an enemy. This was the wrong approach with tinnitus because Gilligan points out, "In fact, a symptom is in part an attempt to repair mind-nature splits. If we can listen deeply to what the symptom is telling us, we no longer need to fear it and try (in vain) to violently destroy it."[25] I did not realise that the subconscious produced the sound was by my to get my attention because it needed the conscious to acknowledge the emotions, something it had not done previously. The sound, unknown to me then, was a sign that I was not connected with myself or centred or grounded emotionally. Later, David taught me that by fully feeling these emotions, there would be no emotional build-up, and tinnitus is unlikely to occur.

Acknowledging What I Resent

There are many people with disabilities; some have disabilities from birth, while others become disabled later. We rarely consider if disabled people are content and what are the emotional and mental effects of their disabilities. Growing up, I was encouraged to make friends with disabled people who had a positive attitude toward their disabilities. These people were active in the disability community and promoted awareness of the disability experience; they favoured the social model of disability, which advocated that disability is socially constructed. I tried to empathise with them since they had a point. However, subconsciously I wanted to get away from this or any identity associated with disability, whether positive or otherwise, and follow my path. There was a limit to the number of disability-related events and speakers I listened to, all spouting the same point.

I Am Just Another Human

I wanted to be a good aunt to my nephew, work towards a fulfilling career, go to the pub with my friends, and do the same stuff that most able-bodied people do. I refused to immerse myself in disability issues or watch every program related to disability because this was simply boring. Ever since I could think for myself, I was discouraged to consider my disability in a negative light. I have not heard of another person with a disability expressing such resentment as I have learned to do in my recovery from emotional trauma. I cannot be the only person who resents their disability. Life presently is marvellous, mainly due to the love and support of my family and friends and the opportunity to study for a Ph.D. and grow as a documentary filmmaker. I would be lying if I said that I do not resent having Cerebral Palsy because I am confined to a body that does not obey my orders. For this reason, before the coronavirus pandemic, Phil regularly took me swimming. It lessens the effects of my disability, making it easier for me to live daily; I love spending time in the water with him. In hypnosis, I learned to open up my tender soft spot, which was closed because of my hatred towards my disability. Gilligan explains this further, "It is a delicate practice to challenge self-intoxication, precisely because it combines both hard and soft parts of the person: the hardness of anger and self-protection, and the softness of the wounded tender soft spot and the fear that the pain will worsen if touched."[26]

I needed to repair what had gone wrong with my past and find a way of living with my disability at an emotional level. Phil helped me do this by spending time with me, which lessened the potency of my disability at an emotional level because he makes me happy and I feel loved.

Although my unexpressed emotional response to my disability resulted in tinnitus when I became an adult, there was a hidden advantage to this. I discovered that when starting my hypnotherapy sessions with David. Yapko says, "Hypnosis empowers people to discover and develop strengths in themselves they didn't know they had, and the consequences in people's lives are often nothing short of extraordinary."[27]

The experience of growing up with a disability taught me to develop courage, determination, resilience, focus, and more, which were assets in the way I learned hypnosis. Of course, this does not imply that I was immune to the feeling of distress, but my experience with hypnosis is an example of how I created a positive outcome. Figley comments that, "It is not uncommon for people who have gone through traumatic events or major catastrophes to experience resilience."[28] What I have done in recovering from tinnitus using hypnosis with David as my guide is what I consider ordinary because of my predisposition to hypnosis. He provided a safe space and presence to fully engage with hypnosis and himself as my therapist, which enabled me to express myself emotionally. David was an attentive listener who offered empathy and understanding, which was vital for processing my trauma.

When I was a girl, I spent most of my life in the company of other disabled people. I did not even hear the faintest murmurs that articulated any bitterness towards their disability and how the medical profession had messed up, leaving an impairment behind. As I became more aware of my disability at an emotional, mental and physical level, I was uncomfortable with what I realised about myself, but I rejected a more comfortable denial. Someone once told me that 'God' had given me a disability to make me a better person. I had never heard of anything more absurd, and I told her such. She replied, I had chosen to have a disability before I was born to experience what it is like, at which point I excused myself and left the room. Yapko states, "In physical disorders where there is no known path to recovery, clinical hypnosis can ease the discomfort, allow some rest, encourage a positive attitude, and lessen any associated emotional trauma. Hypnosis may not facilitate a cure for an illness, but it can still help the person on a variety of levels and in meaningful ways."[29] Hypnosis did not make my physical disability better but provided the resources so that I could cope with it at an emotional level in a much better way.

Through tinnitus, my subconscious was trying to get me to recognise consciously that I hate my disability and that some specific people and events had negatively affected me at an emotional level. Hypnosis taught me to process these emotions consciously and, in time, to let them go so that I could move on with life. However, it was vital for me not to indulge in self-pity or to encourage others to do the same because this mindset is unhelpful in the process of hypnosis and recovery.

Chapter 3

My Disability

I have Cerebral Palsy, in my case, a physical disability that does not allow me to coordinate my muscles, so I use a wheelchair and need twenty-four-hour care. I also have impaired speech, which is understood over time once the listener learns to focus. When I became old enough to sit up, I could not, so I went to a special needs school. In my pushchair, I looked the same as any other kid, and I ran in fields and climbed trees with my brother, but only in my imagination. People often commented that I was a pretty girl with beautiful eyes, but this stopped when my pushchair was replaced with an institutional wheelchair. My wheelchair was comfortable, my house was wheelchair accessible, and my physical needs were taken care of. What drastically went wrong was that although I function normally in my head, my school did not provide the mental, emotional or intellectual support for me to be treated like an ordinary human. The problem was that I was born with a physical disability, not a mental one, but the system did not cater to this particular combination.

Even though the doctors had messed up so badly when I was born, I felt ashamed of having Cerebral Palsy and at what I looked like and how my body moved. I was abashed to go to a special needs school and even more ashamed of what I had to do there. It was demoralising that I could not read, write, walk, dance, or run. I have always been ashamed of my disability but had to realise it through hypnosis. Martina Reynolds and Chris Brewin who research into memory and trauma, write, "Intrusive memories of past events are also common in depression, and are typically memories that bring a sense of shame or humiliation[30]. Such memories can have a profound impact on the person's mood, and also reinforce a negative sense of self, for example as worthless."[31] It was astonishing that my school aimed for nothing higher for me other than holding crayons and scribbling. What effectively the special needs school had done was to turn me into an animal. This meant that I would end up being a social reject, but against all odds, I ended up having a mainstream career instead. I hated celebrating my birthday, and at first, I did not realise why.

Through hypnosis, I discovered that this day was also the anniversary of my acquired Cerebral Palsy. Who would not be traumatised by the experiences I have had to endure? Unsurprisingly, I had tinnitus later in life, resulting from PTSD. When I was a girl, I did not know why I was treated differently from my non-disabled peers. I was not taught to read and write to a level appropriate for my age, and I became convinced that another way of life was waiting out there somewhere. I wanted a life that considered the whole of me, where I could develop my intellect and imagination and put it to some use, and where I would be valued because I had something to offer. As someone with a physical disability, I no longer wanted preferential treatment.

My Mainstream School

A local pressure group's campaign closed down the special needs school, and my life changed for the better. I learned to read and write in a mainstream school when I was seventeen. My first lesson with Peter (my welfare assistant) at the beginning of the Autumn term was Maths. He was shocked to discover how little I knew, and so was the teacher; they were not informed about my background. Peter did not know what to say at first and told me someone should have informed him about my level of education or the lack of it. Peter and I began a programme of education, which included time away from the classroom, where I could learn the basics of Maths and English alongside attending my regular lessons. This was vital since I had no knowledge of basic subjects and had barely learned to read and write. I needed to catch up quickly to pass my GCSEs the following year. When we were alone, Peter divided the time between teaching me Maths and a broader knowledge of English. Often, I would notice him thinking about ways in which he could teach me. His attitude was mature and humorous, as we both knew I had a lot to learn in a short period.

As I enjoyed my new freedom in mainstream society, the conscious memories of the special needs school faded like an old chalk drawing on a blackboard. Upon entering mainstream education, I was released from the special needs cycle of monotony and life going nowhere. There were compromises to be made; I could not sit around and idle time away; there were homework deadlines to meet and the usual pressures of mainstream education. Some of my classmates from my special needs school ended up in other special needs institutions, and while they had a more relaxed pace of life, I geared up for university. This was a long shot, but I had a reasonable chance of making it. However, at an emotional level, it was a different story. I had no reason to reflect on my past negative experiences to consider the emotional impact. Much later and unbeknownst to me, I would have to examine the wreckage of what the special needs system had done so that I could recover from tinnitus.

Life evolves with us, and there is no point in considering what would have happened if circumstances had been different. Now I know that the traumatic experiences of my childhood became the foundation for my particular type of tinnitus. Until I began hypnotherapy as an adult, I could not reflect on the emotional impact of my past or notice the unseen havoc it created in my subconscious.

I am a woman with a physical disability living an able-bodied lifestyle, and I have chosen this life because I rejected the alternative. Like my mother, I am a woman with drive, ambition, and determination to succeed in my career and education. The only way this was possible was to have nothing to do with the special needs system on its metaphorical island; after all, the only thing on offer was occasional coffee mornings and trips to the local day centre. It had taken all my effort to jump off the conveyor belt that led special needs school children to end up in a day centre while the rest of society carried on as usual.

I worked like there was no tomorrow at college and even won an award for being the top media student in the country. I got into university, completed my degree and then a Masters, and then worked as a documentary filmmaker for nine years before starting a Ph.D. There was no time to look back to reflect because the negative experiences of my past provided a reason not to. My conscious was more than happy to block out painful emotional experiences. The past was back there, and I was moving towards a promising future. However, I hardly had the resources to contemplate my emotional state and the effort of avoiding the inevitable future for most disabled people as I was distracted by the tremendous opportunities in my mainstream life.

Not Fitting In

Sometimes, I would encounter another person with a disability, and we would chat for a while, but the more I integrated into mainstream society, the less I had in common with them. Finally, I joined a social club for adults with disabilities and did my best to fit in. The club aimed to encourage people with disabilities to explore and express their sexuality which was taken to the extreme on some occasions. The club's organiser was also a sex therapist, and she arranged a service where people with disabilities could have a visit from a professionally trained prostitute, often to provide them with their first experience of sex (I was not involved in such programmes but just attended the club). Although for some, this may be a defining step into adulthood, I found the whole idea far too uncomfortable. This is one example of how people with disabilities sometimes need to overcompensate. They were nice people, but being with them reminded me too much of my special needs school. On one occasion, after spending a few days on location shooting a documentary with my camera operator, I went to the disability social club. I asked someone how their week had been and what they had done. They responded they had a good week because they went shopping. I had heard similar things from other club members before, and every time I did, it left me with the impression that they had little ambition and self-worth. I had seen something similar in my special needs school and was uncomfortable with the familiarity. This was the final validation that I was not returning, as I did not fit in.

Anything associated with disability made me feel like I was wearing a corset from the Victorian era, and someone had pulled the strings really tight, leaving just enough room for me to breathe. Even though my disability is severe and I am a wheelchair user, I have known for a long time that the disability community and the whole area of disability do not have much to offer me, mentally and emotionally. I have never felt that I have much in common with other disabled people and have struck out on my own to make myself happy. As I grew, I felt exhausted trying to fit into the disability community, but people thought it was the right thing for me to do. I began feeling out of place, and one day I severed the connection between me and those who looked like me.

I Escaped

I did not necessarily do what people expected from someone with my condition. I was certain that if I were to recover from tinnitus, I would need to construct a new lifestyle and mentality; I realised I needed to disconnect from the disability community. At times, some able-bodied people patronised me; for example, I once wanted to open a bank account, so I went to my local branch with my identification and relevant paperwork. I went up in my wheelchair and sat in front of the clerk on the other side of the desk. I told her I was there to open an account while my personal assistant translated. Thinking that I had escaped from one of the local disabled residential homes, she inquired as to which home I had come from and whether they knew I was there. I was unable to open an account that day.

On another occasion, when I had my second Covid vaccination with my female personal assistant, the administrator took our details, such as date of birth, address, and any allergies before vaccination. Then she turned to my personal assistant and asked her if she was pregnant while not inquiring the same from me. I asked her why she did not ask me the same, and she immediately apologised. She must have assumed that I was not sexually active because of my disability. There were other instances where I was not treated as an equal member of society and where the fact that I am a human with emotions, feelings, and intelligence went unrecognised. Some of my friends have felt frustrated and angry on my behalf, but I have to pick my battles. I now have a group of friends; Phil is one of them who provided me with the support, love and care to be who I was meant to be while accepting me as someone who needs a little more physical help. This helped my subconscious and conscious to be in harmony with each other and counteract other people's negative perceptions of me. Sometimes able-bodied people patronise me by undermining my intelligence and not recognising me as someone with autonomy. Nevertheless, the benefits of being in mainstream society greatly outweigh the few who, for whatever reason, do not accept me as an equal. Barack Obama demonstrates the importance of recognising the interconnectedness of us all in his book, *The Promised Land*,

> "In that world – of global supply chains, instantaneous capital transfers, social media, transnational terrorist networks, climate change, mass migration, and ever-increasing complexity – we will learn how to live together, cooperate with one another, and recognize the dignity of others, or we will perish."[32]

Chapter 4

My Mainstream Life

The special needs system or anything related to disability was disorienting and isolated me from reality and what I wanted in life. It limited my perspective and the hopes I had for my future. The breakaway was like the end of a poorly arranged marriage. It was the end of an uncomfortable arrangement made by society that did not recognise that people with disabilities may not enjoy the company of others like them. Whether we think we have a commonality, we all have something in common, but acknowledging that we are individuals with varied preferences is of equal value. It is wrong to segregate certain people because some think they are different. Many years ago, I decided to dissociate from anything to do with disability, apart from the bare minimum essential services like repairing my wheelchair. Until then, I attended disability rights events, thinking it was the right thing to do. These events had speakers with disabilities who would talk about how bad things were for them because of inequality and prejudice from the able-bodied community. The disability rights movement is concerned with oppression, empowerment, and resistance born from how they are treated, but I was bored. They had a fair point, but I had heard this many times before, and it was not solving any problems or helping me. It was time for me to move on to something bigger and to construct a life full of opportunity and happiness; I instinctively knew that mainstream society could offer this to me.

I was honoured when Phil told me to be the Best "Man" at his wedding. Photographer: Paul Broadrick

One of my able-bodied friends once pointed out that I was not in the habit of self-pitying, and they were right; I never saw the point since there is so much to be done in life, and I wanted to get on with achieving my ambitions. Self-pity seems to be a barrier to making friends.

I recollect that on one occasion many years ago, I attended a disability arts event with a panel discussion made up of people with disabilities. The audience, made up of disabled people, asked various questions. Towards the end, I was curious to know whether anyone there who had a disability wanted to work in the mainstream media like myself. I decided to ask the panel and audience, but I was met with a deafening silence that was a few seconds long. No one responded; it was like I had not spoken at all, and then the discussion moved on. After the event, people mingled and socialised, but everyone ignored me as if I was invisible. For many decades, people with disabilities have been marginalised and discriminated against, which is why they find comfort and solidarity in each other and in coming together for a common cause. While I recognise that the able-bodied community should be more accepting of those with disabilities, it would be unfair to blame them entirely. In my experience, disabled people need to make some effort to integrate into mainstream society, as I have done. Whenever I desire to be a part of a group comprising able-bodied people, I go along and find common ground. From my experience, I do not see any issue with being included in mainstream activities which I am enjoying now.

Frequently, people do not even consider my disability and accept me as one of them. That is how I enjoy my life in the mainstream world with my able-bodied friends. I cannot deny how they helped me integrate into mainstream society, enriching my life. I had extricated myself from the special needs system, like a fly removing itself from fly paper. It was painful but possible, and it was worth it.

I am a first-generation Indian, born and raised in the United Kingdom. In general, Indians have a society where a sharply defined identity is rooted in religion and custom. Most Indian people, who call England their home, tend to hang on firmly to their identities while fitting in with the people around them. Religion and tradition meant that many older generations looked down on me. For the most part, when a person is in their early twenties, their parents would want to see them getting married. Other members of the Indian community who had a son or daughter of a similar age would approach other parents to see if they could introduce them to each other. As I hit my twenties, I was not interested in marriage at all, but I was curious to know if anyone would ask after me. Of course, no one did; young men from the community were paired up with women who seemed to have more to offer than I had. This indicated how people in the community generally viewed me; all people offered me was pity and remarks about my disability. As a woman with a disability, society and its norms pushed me inside a box, defining what I ought to do, how I must think, and how I should live an "ideal life". There is a preconceived notion that I am unattractive as a person in a wheelchair with Cerebral Palsy. Often men from the Indian community and the western one have looked at me like I have come from the bottom of their shoe. They are probably the same group who try to push me into a box while being surprised to learn that I have the same needs as them for companionship, love, and the other things that come with a relationship. I fight almost daily against preconceived notions of how my life should be.

Owning her mind and body is unusual for a woman with a physical disability, especially in Indian communities. Having a severe physical disability and being highly educated is a complex issue for most. There are usually two ways people react; denying or not acknowledging that I can understand or treating me as if I have achieved the unimaginable. Perhaps their notions come from their idea of how low the glass ceiling is for people with my level of impairment. Years of experience have taught me that it is fruitless to engage in a conversation that would motivate them to think differently, which is why I appreciate the time I spend with my friends. It has been years since I engaged with the community; there has been a generation or two since my time. Now people are more understanding and accepting towards those with disabilities, but I have moved on, formed lasting friendships, and carved out life outside this community.

No one was interested in a young woman who could not speak and moved like a crazy person, not exactly the ideal daughter-in-law they had in mind. Religion and dogma were a large part of my childhood, where people would refer to my disability negatively. I had been unsuccessful at making friends within the community since people avoided me; it was like I was invisible, except that they never bumped into me. The negative perception of others gradually penetrated and mingled with how I saw myself, and eventually, it was hard to distinguish between the two. This compounded the way I saw myself and, in turn, contributed to tinnitus later on in life.

Fitting In

As a woman of Indian origin and someone with a disability, I fit into neither the Indian community nor the disabled one. At times I felt alone, yet highly invisible, like a feather in the wind, visible and unnoticeable.

Annual walk in Epping forest with the members of The Central London Humanist Group. Photo taken by Mary Grove

My loneliness motivated me to search online for groups I might enjoy attending. I joined the Central London Humanist Group, where I was the only person from an ethnic background at the time, and with a severe disability. I fitted in perfectly, and it was as comfortable as finding the right key to a locked door to friendship and happiness. I met the late Josh Kutchinsky, one of the founders of the Central London Humanist Group, many years ago when I attended my first meeting. When he first saw me in the corner of the meeting room, he introduced himself. My first impressions were that he was warm, polite, friendly, and welcoming. With his wonderful blue eyes, white hair, and beard, he reminded me of Father Christmas. They had an annual general meeting the following January, where they decided to hold all their events in wheelchair-accessible venues so that the group became inclusive. I was amazed at the contrast between this group and what I had experienced in groups before this one. For the first time, I thought this might be what I had been looking for, for so long. I finally entered mainstream society and found genuine friendship and love with it. By this time, there was a new generation in the Indian community which was more aware and accepting of disability, I am not sure if there were any changes in the disabled community, but I had found a new community to belong to and had moved on. On reflection, I have no regrets about abandoning the Indian or the disability community, perhaps I will return to these one day to see how things have changed, but I am in no hurry.

At first, some of my friends found communicating with me a little tricky because of my speech impairment, but with time they became accustomed to the slower-than-normal speech and the way conversations required more time and patience. My friends taught me to see my disability for what it was, a physiological impairment caused by the lack of oxygen at the time of birth and nothing more. Phil pointed out that my body does not do what I want it to do. He articulated what I felt. I thought no one could understand until he expressed it. Of course, I knew this already, but my interaction with most people until now was mostly negative. Some assume the best type of person to understand another with a disability is someone like themselves; my experience has proved the contrary. The Central London Humanist Group organises monthly meetings, allowing me to form friendships and get to know the members well. In the summer, we go on picnics and walk through parks and forests, which I still enjoy. When my nephew was young, I used to bring him with me. It was around the time when I started working on my Ph.D.

One day, I went to a monthly social in the pub with my friends; laughter rose from our table as someone told a story about their school and what happened there one day. 'So what did you get up to in school?' one of my friends looked at me as they spoke. I made my excuses and went to the loo. Upon my return, the subject moved on, and I breathed a great sigh of relief. Charles Figley, an American university professor of traumatology and related fields, suggests that, "Survivors are often reluctant to talk-either out of fear of traumatizing other family members, or as a manifestation of avoidance."[33] Many years ago, I left the special needs education system behind. While most people have memorabilia from their school years, I have none. I decided to get rid of it all except for a couple of school reports locked away in my filing cabinet. I have no idea why I still have them. In one of the reports, the teacher remarked how surprised he was that I was able to tell the time on a twenty-four-hour clock and could count money; I was turning sixteen when this report was written. Numerous similar memories and experiences would sound absurd to the ears of the able-bodied, but they are too painful for me to recall.

As I looked at my friends laughing and joking in a pub on that Wednesday night, I felt grateful that none of these was a part of my present mainstream life. Nevertheless, memories and emotions from my past were incarcerated in my subconscious, desperate to be let out. The louder they knocked and shouted, the more my conscious mind reinforced the barriers that prevented me from acknowledging the subconscious part of myself that I was unaware existed. Even though they had something important to say, I did not know how to listen. So they blared like sirens, blasting through the door to my conscious, hoping to grab my attention; every voice was an earthquake. I felt desperately unwell, but did not know why.

One more step and you're falling into the darkness of your subconscious
mind

where people fear to tread all the time

my ears become accustomed to the prisoners behind closed doors

chanting their stories of me

what are they saying? I wonder

but their voices all merge into one

there are now cries of pain from my subconscious mind

which I don't recognise but I hear them all the time

even when I'm asleep

the past doesn't talk, they say but if you listen carefully, it does

so I listened carefully with care, like they were really there

and they disappeared in the night one by one and my job was done

Definitions

Before you continue reading this book, I provide definitions of the subconscious and hypnosis since I refer to both terms throughout my writing.

Conscious Defined

The conscious is a series of learned concepts with the ability to organize themselves, and to understand the continuous influx from our senses to make sense of the world. As children, we learn to have an identity and to understand who we are because our parents and immediate environment shape this understanding of our self-concept; this concept of ourselves is formed in the conscious. The physical evolution of the human brain is glacial, taking tens of thousands of years for any noticeable change. Yet, humanity has often taken considerable strides to improve our skills, often happening in a single generation. Thomas Blakeslee, an author and researcher, believes that acquiring new understandings of the world and our relationship to it alters our self-concept. The key to these rapid changes is not brain alterations, but self-concept modifications.[34] The conscious experience is one thing we are certain about as it comes with being alive; our senses continuously provide the conscious with information about the immediate environment. Many religions believe that whatever we feel or experience is an illusion. I do not think it would be wise to adopt this view; for example, as I write this, I am aware that I am thinking about the choice of words that I use to convey my thoughts, and I am also aware that my dog has entered the room. This is my experience of being alive right now. Throughout this book, there are references to the conscious, which may provide you with further insights to what the conscious is; it should be noted that I have used the lens of hypnosis for this.

Subconscious Defined

We imagine the subconscious is out of reach and its own entity that we, as conscious beings, do not fully understand; in fact, the subconscious is not abstract or inaccessible to us. We are able to move to a world of pure imagination from the quantum world of creative light. The subconscious is beyond the common definitions of time and space and is without form. We can explore unlimited possibilities, and create new realities because there is a superposition, which is a wave in the subconscious, where all possible states are stored, past, present and possible futures.[35] This is why we rely on the subconscious when we need new perspectives on life and when we might be stuck without knowing how to do things differently or better and more in line with what we actually want. When we tap into the subconscious, new possibilities are apparent, making life richer and more diverse.

Hypnosis Defined

All too often, in the media's portrayal of hypnosis, we may see someone performing extraordinary feats, like plunging an arm into ice-cold water while claiming not to experience pain. The true purpose of hypnosis is to allow us to reconnect with ourselves at a deep, emotional level, but most people do not know how. Therefore, in my journey to rediscover my true subconscious self, I had to learn to understand myself at this level.

According to Yapko,

> "The unconscious is, metaphorically speaking, a reservoir of all the multidimensional experiences acquired throughout your lifetime, including your

historical experience, personal and social learnings, manner (drives, motivations, needs) for interacting with your world, and maintaining your automatic functioning in countless behaviors each day, from breathing to digesting to adjusting how you're sitting. The unconscious is capable of responding to implications and symbolic interpretations, not just what is said but also what might be heard 'between the lines' of what is said."[36]

Hypnosis is difficult to define, as Yapko suggests, "Scholars have grappled with the issue from the earliest days of hypnosis. Even long-time practitioners have an easier time describing rather than defining hypnosis."[37]

My journey with hypnosis has been remarkable, as it enables deep engagement at an emotional level, below conscious awareness. When I thought there were no answers, hypnosis provided so many. Yapko further explains hypnosis,

"What hypnosis does best is amplify people's abilities, including their hidden abilities such as the capacity to reduce the subjective experience of pain or the capacity to better adapt to a change in their circumstance. Hypnosis empowers people to discover and develop strengths in themselves they didn't know they had, and the consequences in people's lives are often nothing short of extraordinary."[38]

Hypnosis gave me insights to all my experiences and their associated emotions, which I did not realise even existed because they were below conscious awareness. Stephen Gilligan explains hypnosis, "Generative trance is not a traditional hypnosis where one gives up control or consciousness, but a creative art in which conscious and unconscious minds are woven into a higher consciousness capable of creativity and transformation."[39] Waterfield, a historian of hypnosis, suggests that hypnosis allows us to withdraw our attention from the outside world, making it possible to focus on fewer stimuli.[40] The 'conscious' mind is whatever contents of consciousness are in the spotlight at that moment. We have the facility to move the 'beam of awareness' around and light up different areas of the mind - thus, what we call subconscious is essentially all that is not illuminated by awareness at a specific moment. Yapko suggests that, "Rather than there being a specific, unique location for the experience of hypnosis in the brain, the direction and intensity of attention and the types of mental activities encouraged will determine which areas of the brain are likely to be actively involved."[41]

As a person explores their psychological landscape, the beam becomes more expansive, and the areas of the mind grow. This is how the subconscious can become conscious.

Through this process, I could discover all that caused my emotional trauma and deal with it appropriately. In my journey of recovering from tinnitus, hypnosis allowed me to explore the subconscious through the conscious, fostering communication between the two; so, the conscious understood the subconscious. Gilligan outlines the three states of consciousness,

> "(1) a "pure consciousness" world of creative love
> and light; (2) a "quantum world" of the creative

unconscious, with infinite possibilities and pure imagination; and (3) the classical world of the conscious mind, with its consciousness of time-space, matter, and other "reality" elements."[42]

David Corr, my hypnotherapist, has been deeply influenced by Milton Erickson's approach to hypnosis and has spent time learning from Stephen Gilligan, who was Erickson's student. In writing this book, I feel indebted to all three of them for the wisdom of hypnosis and their ingenious approach to applying this in their practice.

Chapter 5

Having a Medical Diagnosis & The Effect of my Emotions Closing Down

I firmly believe that mental health issues should be as easy and acceptable to discuss as physical health problems. When I was diagnosed with tinnitus, I was told there was no chance of recovery. My regular emotions receded, causing tinnitus, which impacted my daily interactions. I had feelings of loneliness, depression, anxiety, and desperation all at the same time. I needed to behave as if nothing was wrong. Why? I will explain that later in the chapter.

Diagnosis and the Hospital

We live in a society where it is almost normal for people to talk about being unwell and visiting the hospital. The person listening may express sympathy and concern, perhaps enquiring further, even offering help and support. When it comes to mental health, though, the story is different. I have been told to pull myself together, to get over it, that it could all be fixed by a good night's sleep, that I have a weak mind and that there are so many people who are worse off than I am, and that I should show gratitude for what I have. This is not logical since the mind is as fragile as the body, and sometimes things do go wrong at a psychological level.

Medical Professionals

I went to the hospital and, after being asked a few questions, I was given a big, blue form that said I had tinnitus in the left ear. They also handed me a bunch of leaflets about tinnitus, which was supposed to help me but did not. The information on tinnitus failed to make the association and the suppression of emotions or PTSD. There is a clear distinction between tinnitus caused by physical damage to the inner ear and tinnitus caused by PTSD and the suppression of emotions. A report by a neurologist stated that I apparently had a severe learning disability and delayed milestones, but it also mentioned that I was undertaking a Ph.D. This is one example where medical professionals seem to contradict themselves and appear to be confused and unfocused on the issue of tinnitus. If the medical profession had a more holistic approach, considering my psychological and physiological needs, they might have deduced whether psychological treatment would help. Waterfield substantiates this by claiming, "We live in a materialistic age: faced with something that can be prodded by a scalpel, doctors assume that a scalpel is what they had better use."[43]

The failure of medical professionals to investigate other possible causes and treatments of tinnitus demonstrates their lack of recognising the importance of a person's mental health and emotional well-being. Even though I was talking to a man in a lab coat in a hospital, it hurt to know that no treatments were available. I felt angry and frustrated, as if someone had slammed me into a brick wall. When I went home, I asked myself how I could live with this noise, and it baffled me when I thought about how other people had learned to live with it. I went to bed anguished and stayed there until the following day.

Both medicine and religion, whether eastern or western, encourage us to think that the body and the mind or soul are separate entities and cannot be treated as one. Medical diagnosis starts and ends with the physical body, and most medical professionals often disregard the psychological aspects that make us individuals.

As professor Geoffrey Samuel, an emeritus professor of religious studies at Cardiff University and Jay Johnston, who has written extensively about religion, explain,

> "Virtually all human cultures known to us have some kind of concept of mind, spirit or soul as distinct from the physical body, if only to explain experiences such as sleep and dreaming...This tendency, while often associated with the French philosopher René Descartes, has deep roots in Western, and specifically Christian, thought, with its characteristic opposition of spiritual and material concerns. Such dichotomizing tends to lead to a materialist reduction on the one side, an idealist rejection of the world on the other, and leaves little room for a messy and complex reality that arguably includes not only the extremes, but much in between."[44]

After all, no one exists only as a physical body; we are also emotional beings that feel and have emotions that can and do get damaged and need care and repair. The medical profession failed to realise that a complicated psychological process had started in my childhood, the tail end of which was the cause of my tinnitus. Hypnosis takes a holistic approach to treatment; it considers our emotional state, how and why we have become the person we are today, and how our psychological damage can be repaired even when it is under the radar of the conscious. One of the many benefits of hypnosis is that it examines and treats the roots of problems that may not even have entered our conscious awareness and identifies their source. My ordeal could have been shortened if the medical profession had better understood the subconscious and hypnosis. Doctors' resistance to hypnosis makes them blind to other treatments, limiting perspectives to the physical body. The medical profession wants to maintain control and authority, while hypnosis hands control back to the patient.

As psychotherapist and hypnotherapist Dr. Jeffrey Zeig, trained under Erickson, writes, "Our only tool is ourselves. In order to communicate therapeutically, one needs to grow increasingly aware of the effect of one's message and the effect one's message can have."[45] The knowledge of hypnosis and how and when to apply it has been vital in my recovery from tinnitus, providing me with an understanding of the appropriate hypnotherapy exercises. I also gained responsibility and control over my recovery.

Emotions Closing Down

Just before the onset of tinnitus, I constantly felt numb and had lost the ability to provide an emotional response. I had also lost the desire to care about anything while feeling detached and disinterested in life as if it was meaningless. I avoided reminiscing about my past and how I got to where I was, and I could not contemplate my future either. This meant I was trapped in the present, which is different from living in the moment. Studies found that mental time travel is common[46], which indicates that my inability to do this was unusual, suggesting that something was wrong. At this time, I was unsure about the reason for my numbness, but later on, David helped me realise that this resulted from my emotions ceasing to work. The trauma I experienced in my childhood as an adult caused my normal emotions to recede. A feeling of numbness towards my past and avoiding thinking about it was natural to someone experiencing PTSD. One aim of hypnosis is to re-explore my past at an emotional level to realise how I actually felt at the time and to acknowledge my current feelings.

Arnaud d'argembeau is an Associate Professor at the University of Liège and Senior Research Associate for the Fund for Scientific Research, whose primary research interest is in the cognitive and neural bases of autobiographical memory and future-oriented thinking. He found that, "...autobiographical memory retrieval is a protracted process in which general knowledge about one's past (general events and lifetime periods) is used to access specific memories."[47] It is important to be flexible when thinking about the future because this allows you to grow as a person and develop your potential while simultaneously being logical, consistent, and stable. When people imagine their future, emotional elements can have an emotionally powerful and lasting impression.[48] In my case, I could neither contemplate my future nor feel any emotions associated with it. It was as if I was locked into the present with no way to feel any emotions at all. These are symptomatic of depression[49], and since I did not experience anything different, I took this feeling as normal. Research suggests that an important role of episodic memory is to help to create circumstances of future imagined scenarios. This happens by fetching information from the subconscious concerning past experiences, with the flexibility to recombine segments of what happened in the past into reproducing future simulations.[50] These future musings are informed by what happened to us in the past; for example, I had experiences with other disabled people when I was a child, which were mostly negative and may explain why as an adult, I enjoy the company of able-bodied people.

Emotions are necessary to keep us safe and interact with other people to build relationships with those around us. They also help us have an emotional opinion about our treatment by them. It is vital to experience the entire spectrum of emotions, even those we consider negative. These so-called negative emotions, in particular, are vital in keeping us safe concerning other people, but more critically, in my case, in relation to tinnitus. My ability to suppress these emotions caused the tinnitus to become louder and was the main reason that tinnitus occurred. If someone became angry with me, I would feel nothing at all; I did not feel anger or recognise injustice, which caused the tinnitus to increase. Later in this book, on p. 264, I describe how it was possible to relearn how to feel emotions consciously, so I no longer felt numb.

Sometimes we stop ourselves from feeling so-called 'bad' emotions to avoid feeling down or sad in the moment. In my case, this became a habit where the conscious would actively be a barrier to these emotions surfacing. For example, when I was in a situation where the appropriate response was to feel anger, this emotion would express itself consciously as frustration. When I ought to have felt frustration, I simply felt sad. This meant that each emotion was diluted and not completely felt at a conscious level. The remainder was stuck in the subconscious, probably because of the neuromuscular lock described on p. 72. As a result, these emotions expressed themselves through vivid dreams, while in wakefulness, my emotional reactions to what I experienced were felt in a diluted form.

Other People

I had learned to disguise that I was seriously unwell to avoid people providing unhelpful but well-meaning advice. For example, some suggestions included taking a nap, having a hot drink, watching a good show, or reading a magazine for entertainment. All of these became impossible when thunder roared in my head, something I knew was fruitless to explain. Their advice and the suppression of expressing how I felt added to the stress that tinnitus caused. Regardless, it was less stressful when people left me alone since tinnitus is unwounded torture. It felt like I was imprisoned, but this confinement was inconspicuous to others.

I had an overwhelming feeling of being in a car and being aware that it was about to crash. Though the car never crashed, the feeling that something dreadful and catastrophic was about to happen repeated itself over a few minutes daily. This gave rise to panic attacks, where I felt overwhelmingly anxious when there was no reason. I overcame these feelings by rationalising my situation to a point where I realised there was no reason to panic, at which point the feeling subsided.

Even though it is impossible to know precisely what another person is feeling, by denying their experience of pain, you also downplay the perception of their suffering. You may cause them to deny how they feel and imagine their suffering is exaggerated, even when this is not the case. The denial of my emotions and feelings was one of the main things that caused my tinnitus to increase in volume; in effect, the subconscious needed the converse.

Through hypnosis, I learned that traumatic childhood experiences taught me to suppress negative emotions as a coping mechanism, which was the reason for my tinnitus as an adult. On p. 171, I describe a way of releasing major negative experiences that were the foundation of my tinnitus. As mentioned in the Introduction, unaddressed trauma from the past, which has not been processed consciously, may lead to tinnitus.

As psychoanalyst Sándor Ferenczi, a contemporary of Freud, wrote, "Memory is...a collection of scars of shocks in the ego."[51] Trauma leaves long-lasting scars in the subconscious even when the original experience has been forgotten at a conscious level. It becomes crucial to abandon the primitive and ego levels to understand the subconscious and to access the emotional knowledge within it. This is because hypnosis is an ongoing process of connecting, reconnecting, and acknowledging what the subconscious offers regarding emotional knowledge about ourselves at a level more profound than the conscious.

When I was a young girl, a relative would give me sweets, but they would also make patronising comments. It would be easy for me to recall the person giving me sweets, though I would forget that they also patronised me. My subconscious, however, did not forget the trauma caused. Yapko says, "What we decide is important, but *how* we decide is even more important. This is what I call the art of discrimination, the ability to make a good choice in a given situation utilising both insight and foresight."[52] Being so young, I could not express what I was feeling, even though I was aware of my experience at the time. Unlike the biological mechanisms that regulate our body, like the beating of our hearts or the function of our kidneys, which are performed automatically and below conscious awareness, what happens to us on the outside needs to be experienced rather than ignored. We must be witnesses and participate in our experiences from moment to moment to feel and acknowledge them in totality. Recovery occurs when the conscious acknowledges the trauma of the emotional reality from the past and stops selectively editing it.

I consciously denied painful emotions because I had not learned to process difficult emotions and feelings. The environment in my special needs school neither encouraged emotional expression nor did it provide emotional support. We were simply cattle with the daily routine of sustaining life. I further explain my experience in a special needs school in Chapter 6. The subconscious stores memories and associated emotions in their entirety, while the conscious is selective. Cognitive neuroscientists, Michael C. Anderson and Benjamin J. Levy, from the Memory Control Lab at Cambridge University, suggest that selective retrieval is an "...instance of response override in memory that occurs when a cue is related to a strong, prepotent memory that is not currently desired."[53]

They further suggest,

> "...sometimes stopping retrieval can itself be the person's primary goal. In these instances, we simply wish to stop retrieval from occurring. For example, when glimpsing an image of a loved one who has recently passed away we may marshal our efforts to stop painful thoughts of loss from coming into awareness."[54]

This is a mechanism the conscious uses to prevent us from feeling overwhelmed in situations beyond our control. However, if this is sustained over a long period, this results in losing the ability to feel emotions of any kind, especially the so-called negative ones.

Time Of The Month

As a woman, I have found menstruation difficult, mainly because of my physical disability. The onset of a period would contribute to my tinnitus becoming extremely loud, doubling in volume for this duration. It was impossible to hear another person talk, and I felt particularly alone and suicidal. In addition, I did not experience premenstrual stress like before I had tinnitus which leads me to assume that the premenstrual emotions that I otherwise would have felt were suppressed in the subconscious, which contributed to the tinnitus becoming louder.

Neuromuscular Lock

As a physically disabled child in a special needs school, I was actively discouraged from engaging emotionally to the extent of not questioning and protesting about my circumstances and treatment. It was the status quo where all the children, including me, were kept mindlessly occupied while I desired ambition, purpose, and knowledge. This encouraged the suppression of my trauma, as no one in authority was listening; the conscious is highly efficient at editing out trauma, but the unedited emotional reality remains in the subconscious. When the conscious does this over a long period, this becomes dangerous. This is how my tinnitus started, but this emotional suppression may express itself in other forms in other people, which is a form of post-traumatic stress disorder, explained on p. 108.

When emotional trauma is experienced but not expressed, the subsequent unacknowledged emotions are repressed back into the subconscious or expressed in a highly diluted form, so the entire emotion is not felt completely. Gilligan calls this a 'Neuromuscular lock' and explains this problem further: "Neuromuscular lock traps

72

consciousness in a fixed and disconnected reality, giving rise to tremendous suffering and problems."[55]

The conscious becomes a strict gatekeeper, confining emotions and any associated painful memories to the subconscious. Professor Gerald Clore of the University of Virginia believes that "...while the cognitive processing that causes the emotion is unconscious, the informational and motivational effects of emotion depend on conscious experience in order to capture the attention of the experiencer..."[56]

He further explains that to be aware of the presence of emotions, we must feel them consciously.[57] As a result of trauma, the neuromuscular lock prevents negative emotions from entering the conscious, which is why they remain at the subconscious level. When we are in this state, we are unreceptive to new experiences and shut down emotionally. If a person is in neuromuscular lock for a significant amount of time, like I was, they may not be aware of this barrier. In this state, emotions may remain unprocessed in the somatic self, which is in no man's land between the conscious and the subconscious.[58]

All of this erodes the connection between the subconscious and the conscious. This is akin to trying to make a telephone call to someone only to find that their telephone is constantly engaged. When this happens, emotional messages from the subconscious fail to be acknowledged consciously. In other words, the bridge between the subconscious and the conscious is broken, isolating thoughts and emotions that were supposed to follow from memories and recent experiences on the island of the subconscious. This results in subconscious emotions being expressed in other ways, in my case, in the form of tinnitus. Therefore, we must learn to traverse the land of knowing to the land of realising by using hypnosis to build a bridge between the two. This is how emotions return to connect with our conscious memories, completing the circuit and making us whole. This book retells how I could rebuild this bridge brick by brick which returned me to silence, back to better mental health.

The aim of hypnosis and, indeed, this book is to provide a variety of mechanisms to reverse conscious emotional suppression. The landscape of my subconscious had retained memories that I had forgotten consciously, while the conscious remained emotionally impoverished because of the traumatic experiences of my childhood. Suppression is when trauma encourages the conscious to build a barrier between the subconscious and itself, where emotions are trapped in the subconscious behind this barrier. When this happened, I lost the ability to access my emotions when I needed them, and I could not bring them up to the conscious level where I could feel them. Hypnosis provided a solution to this, a way of breaking down the barrier between the subconscious and the conscious. Emotions, trapped like caterpillars in the subconscious were finally allowed to evolve naturally into butterflies to be acknowledged and released through the conscious. Metaphorically speaking, I came to life when I joined mainstream society via the back door. No one noticed where I came from or how I entered.

And in the dark heart of the ancient past
there was a story of a little girl there who wouldn't last
for it was the last night in hell
I didn't believe it that she survived completely
and on the way back from there she tripped and fell over life

and no one was there to pick her up

not even when she scraped her knee

so she wrote an accurate history book of her past

no one believed her but she didn't care

for as a woman now the history books were meant for her a permanent

record of the nightmares that came true but it was only for her you see

to remind her of her reality

for she would burn those books if she could but she didn't want to really

she would forget to acknowledge the truth and deny facts about herself

and then the nightmares would start again in her mind's eye and she

wanted to move forwards and not backwards in life for the past cannot

collide with the future now

for if it did she would surely slide down to hell again and anyway who

would believe her again?

So with courage, she marched forwards in life

not even looking back once or twice

for words failed her as she spoke about the past

so she shut up for she knew she wouldn't last

and so as she entered through the back door of society

no one saw her come in as she joined it and when they asked her about

the past

she was vague about that for she didn't want to be judged

she just wanted the past to fade away

but she would be known as the woman with no history

but that was all right according to her

As I have mentioned in the Introduction, some people with disabilities may end up in residential homes and institutions. I wanted to lead a more mainstream life by getting an education and following my career aspirations, but I paid a heavy emotional price for it. The time and effort required to do this distracted me from acknowledging the past and realising the impact of my childhood as a disabled person, the social exclusion, and the subsequent emotional trauma that came with that.

On my journey to recovery, I discovered a considerable amount of trauma from my past and had to re-engage with it along the way. Some people find the negative emotions associated with memories too traumatic to rediscover fully. For me, the trauma was having to live with tinnitus. In any case, I did not want all that trauma to be stuck inside me; I cannot imagine why anyone would want this. Hypnosis provided a guided tour of how life works and the mechanisms and processes of how we are human today. I had a front-row seat to the hidden unconscious emotions that pull us like puppets. It was privileged access and a painful one too. In returning to silence, I defy the prognosis given to me by the medical profession, which believes that it is not possible to recover from tinnitus and that this condition needs to be endured and managed for a lifetime. As a by-product, my love for hypnosis was born.

Chapter 6

The Importance of Acknowledging my Trauma

The pressure of being expected to act normally by those around me caused my regular emotions to recede, impacting my daily interactions. I will present some related childhood memories and how they contributed to my bad mental health. As described previously, my emotions were closing down due to my inability to process the trauma of the past. The more this happened, the louder the tinnitus became until the noise was as loud as a jet engine. I felt numb to all that I encountered. This was the extreme reaction to not processing the painful emotional experiences of my childhood.

In The Beginning

Margaret Thatcher was appointed the Secretary of State for Education in 1970. She formulated the Committee of Enquiry for the Education of Handicapped Children and Young People, which the Labor government maintained in 1974. This ensured that all children and young people with a disability had a right to education. The purpose of this committee was to ensure that every child had access, and the aim was to imagine a future where every child could experience enjoyment, understanding, and independence. It was relatively smooth for able-bodied children, but for those with disabilities, it required the removal of obstacles to achieve the same goal.[59] Local authorities were and still are uncertain about what to do with children with disabilities.

My parents and brother came to settle in England in the seventies, and I was born a few months later. Being new to the country was stressful enough, but one can not imagine the shock of being told their baby had brain damage. When I was growing up in the 1970s and 1980s, special needs schools, giving specialised care to children with disabilities, were prominent throughout the United Kingdom. My parents relied on professionals to help and guide them about provisions for me; after all, they were the 'experts'. So, for example, they believed I should attend a special needs nursery and then a school for children with disabilities in the same borough.

Children born with complications that led to a disability and children who developed disabilities could survive with the advancement of medicine. Special needs schools welcomed such children whom the mainstream might have discarded. Hence, schools like the one I attended were a cauldron of disabilities. Undoubtedly, most families, I imagine, were grateful for their children to have somewhere to go where their basic needs were met by staff with the time and the expertise to offer. However, I saw my special needs school through a very different lens.

My self-awareness grew over time, and I knew it was wrong to be segregated from my able-bodied peers because it was unfair to take the same approach with every disabled child based on their physical ability. The special needs system gave free rein to my teachers, who, though thought to be the best people to provide me with individual care and attention, failed to understand my learning capabilities. As much as I attempted to explain that I had ambitions and the ability to learn, I felt my emotions and feelings were not respected or acknowledged. Those in authority seemed just as susceptible to their own biases as everyone else; after all, they were human. What sets those who think differently, is their ability to see that another way is possible, despite the majority thinking in a certain way. Both as a child and as an adult, I think differently from others. Most people go with the odds since doubts trigger disbelief only if you cannot explain them away. It was easy for most children and their parents to follow the line of thinking that the teachers in my special needs school promoted, probably because the teachers themselves had a genuine belief in their system.

Back then, it was improbable that someone with my kind of disability would go to university and have a career, making those in authority default to thinking in a way that was most comfortable for them. I was different, but I was powerless to make myself heard. I was surrounded by people who did not know how to think big; this meant that I was being tugged in a direction I did not want to go. The message from this, I guess was that I had to surrender to whatever was my fate. The trouble was that this 'fate' was predetermined by a society and education system that had very different ideas from the way I envisioned my life and future. It was an invisible tug of war, one which affected me deep down at a subconscious level. My experience taught me that we might fail even if we believe we could transform those strangers who are in control of us through reason or evidence. If you are a parent or guardian of a child with disabilities and if you put them in a special needs school, that does not make you a bad or incompetent person. You might just have defaulted to the way of thinking encouraged by a society that likes to put everyone in boxes with labels because it is easier and seems logical on one level.

Swimming against the tide is much more challenging. Still, in my case, the reason I have a Ph.D. despite what happened to me was not that I am not some kind of "supercrip" overcoming the odds; it is because had I been able-bodied, I probably would have gone to university anyway. What makes me unique in the eyes of others is that I have done what I have done despite being at a disadvantage. The hardship of going through so much for something so commonplace as an education and a career could have been avoided if those in positions of authority had broadened their concept of "normal". I believe that even society is guilty of this too. There is no clairvoyant ability to peer into those we see as different, so we need restraint and humility. What I have experienced is too familiar to some people, disabled or not.

I walked along the road to nowhere and got lost along the way
the compass in my head was broken
I stumbled
tripped
and fell over life itself and scraped my knee
"ouch!" I said
"what's this?" I asked
dreams tumbled over into dreams
words fell out of my mouth as if desperate to escape
I stopped them, and this is why I died inside
my future was sealed now in a special needs vacuum
I entered neverland where special needs children never grew up
and in the dark heart of the ancient past
there was a story of a little girl there who wouldn't last
for it was the last night in hell
I didn't believe it that she survived completely

and on the way back from there she tripped and fell over life

and no one was there to pick her up

not even when she scraped her knee

so she wrote an accurate history book of her past

no one believed her but she didn't care

for as a woman now the history books were meant for her

a permanent record of the nightmares that came true but

it was only for her

to remind her of her reality

for she would burn those books if she could

but she didn't want to really

for she would forget to acknowledge the truth

and deny facts about herself

and then the nightmares would start again in her mind's eye

she wanted to move forwards and not backwards in life

for the past cannot collide with the future now

for if it did she would surely slide down to hell again

anyway who would believe her again?

So with courage she marched forwards in life

not even looking back once or twice

for words failed her as she spoke about the past

so she shut up for she knew she wouldn't last

so as she entered through the back door of society

no one saw her come in as she joined it

when they asked her about the past

she was vague about that for she didn't want to be judged

she just wanted the past to fade away

but she would be known as the woman with no history

but that was all right according to her

and became a stone statue

but fires burned behind numbness

To write this book, I have been going through a bunch of reports from my special needs school and independent bodies, and it was quite a challenge to understand their perspective. On the one hand, the consensus was that I was a child with average intelligence. Still, all professionals seemed to hesitate to confirm that I should have access to a mainstream and age-appropriate curriculum. This closed-loop seemed to repeat every year with the same professionals. It was easy for them to acknowledge my intelligence, but when it came to giving me practical support, they seemed reluctant.

Anna Abraham, who is a Professor in Creativity and Gifted Education at the University of Georgia, Athens, and has an interest in mental time travel, creativity, and imagination, says, "Humans have a remarkable ability to navigate the social environment by going beyond perceptual, social cues to infer more complex hidden mental states of others, including their thoughts, beliefs, feelings, desires, and intentions..."[60] The reports from the teachers also lack foresight about what I might be capable of achieving; for example, going to university or having a career are not mentioned. Their attitude indicated a lack of ambition for my future, which was below my conscious awareness at the time. It ran through undertones of every interaction they had with me, which I was sensitive enough to pick up but not articulate enough to describe in words.

The reports seem to be written with thoroughness and detail, but at the same time, there is no vision for my future within them. For example, one report commented on my ability to recognise currency and add it together; I was fifteen at the time. It is easy to see how minimal expectations stopped me from moving forward emotionally, mentally, or psychologically. Another report mentions that "she is sometimes reticent to try new topics." My reluctance was because I knew that what they offered would not lead to a better future, but my teachers interpreted this as stubbornness. I did not see the point in considering their unbelievably low expectations, but they did not seem to comprehend this. Educational psychologists tested me annually and concluded that I seemed to have above-average intelligence. When I look back on these reports, I am struck by how those uncommitted professionals did not make it possible for me to reach my full potential, but only seemed to be skilled at writing reports that served no purpose in improving my life opportunities.

I had a greater awareness of the effects of my environment on my mental deterioration than the teachers, psychologists, and other children. From the age of eleven, I was moved to a class of children older than me every year in the vain hope that this would be adequate for my intellectual needs. I was moved two grades on average every year, while the other students were moved by one grade. Soon I was in a class with children three years older than me, yet the work was mind-numbingly easy.

My special needs school was a happy place with teachers and welfare staff dedicating their days and careers to us, the special needs ones. Children of multiple faith observed birthdays, Easter, Christmases, and even Diwali, a Hindu festival and other religious occasions. The teachers encouraged the children to make festive decorations and cards to be put up in the classrooms and for their families. Being of Hindu parentage, Diwali was an excuse for me to stay home. No one minded, and I did not care if I was missed. I wanted a mainstream future with a decent education and days to look forward to. Every second was a second lost, young lives destroyed or kept occupied depending on your point of view; I thought the former. I recognised the pointlessness of it all; it was a dead-end when childhood should have been about learning and growth.

I was tired of being bored and undermined by the teachers, but they never recognised that I was capable of mainstream education. I assumed the staff did not understand my full potential or my aspirations of going to university. At the time, the notion of my attending university seemed incomprehensible to others. I lacked sufficient education and did not have the basic ability to read or write; I was also severely physically disabled. It seemed like I was the only one aware of my average intelligence, which gave me confidence that I could attend university one day, and I constantly imagined myself as a university student. Abraham suggests, "From a future-oriented perspective, repeated rehearsal of a positive vision of oneself in the future has been investigated as a means to increase general optimism about the future..."[61] According to scientific studies, when we continue to have positive mental imagery of ourselves, it becomes more likely that whatever we imagine will come to pass through the automatic activation of emotional states and the way we behave through our responses.[62]

Glimpsing Without Seeing

My special needs school had two playgrounds, one for the primary children and one for those over thirteen. The former was surrounded on three sides by the school building. A wall about knee height was on the fourth side, overlooking the road, with a hedge above it. I would often look through the small gaps and see the footpath and the road beyond. I glimpsed people walking by and listened to their footsteps and chatter, but I never saw them completely. I became trapped by my conscious. This was an apt description of the limitations of my life's perspective and the world beyond. I forgot that there was a world outside the special needs system. I was experiencing, without comprehending, the implications of being excluded from mainstream life. After lunch, the dinner ladies would mindlessly push children in wheelchairs around the playground, following the same path repeatedly. I did not comprehend that I was trapped.

> *I never knew the wisdom inside me grew like a tree*
> *it was there all along*
> *many people want a second opinion on life*
> *but I burn to be left alone so that I could listen to the wisdom in my head*
> *and it said you don't belong here; your transformation isn't complete*
> *I turned into a doll sitting on a shelf somewhere*
> *and with unblinking eyes I stared while a tornado grew inside my mind's eye*
> *I wanted to fly but I couldn't*
> *so the special needs system picked me up and played with me*
> *and then left me on a shelf to rot with other dolls*

Going Up In The World

The special needs school had two departments. The main block was for children under sixteen, and a department in another building, like a further education development, was for young adults over sixteen. When I was fourteen, I began communicating with a teacher in this department and explained to them that the work was too easy and I was frustrated in the main school. I continued having this dialogue over a few months, after which they agreed I could move there. I was delighted at being challenged and thought it would be exciting to be in a class with people two years my senior. However, I was disappointed in the first hour of arriving there, as the work was ridiculously simple, easier than the main school. What disturbed me the most was these pupils, although post-sixteen, had various learning difficulties as well as physical challenges. It dawned on me like a nightmare that it was actually a department for life skills training. The aim was to teach pupils with mild and moderate learning disabilities how to cope with daily tasks, such as shopping, cooking, basic communication, and looking after money. I knew how to manage money at eight, as my dad had been a shopkeeper most of his life, and I used to sit with him after school and see the customers who exchanged money for our goods; it was second nature for me. As for cooking, they did this for me since I was unable to use my hands. We also had an utterly pointless environmental enrichment class for two hours a week, where we needed to describe the relationships between different shapes in a diagram. For example, if a diagram had a triangle, a circle, and a square next to each other in a row, we had to describe that the circle was between the triangle and the square. The teacher seemed to enjoy praising me for my amazing ability to do remarkably well; I still cannot figure out what intellectual benefit was meant to be derived from this lesson.

The Teaching Willow Tree

One day, as I was going across to the other building from the main school in my electric wheelchair, I paused under a big beautiful willow tree. It was spring, and the leaves started to show on the branches that formed a giant umbrella over me. As I looked up at the branches, I wondered whether this was what life was about. I silently asked the willow to give me an answer even though I  had figured out by now that trees could not talk, but on reflection, that was the first piece of hypnosis I had ever done. The space between the main school and the other building provided time for thought, and I realised I was looking for the answer within myself. Later, with David, I learned that "In training oneself to be skilled in experiencing hypnosis or self-hypnosis, one is learning how to regulate one's attentional abilities."[63] This is how my ideas about life formed. In the act of wondering, I knew what was happening to me was wrong. Later on, I realised that with hypnosis, it was impossible for me to be alone since I had my subconscious to befriend and support me.

Not Learning to Communicate

The environment in my special needs school was substandard and unequipped to teach me communication skills because most of the other children had learning disabilities. The teachers did not realise that I could speak and that my intellect was in full working order. They comprehended that I had a physical disability, which includes speech impairment. However, I was in the same class as children with learning disabilities and the activities in the class met their needs rather than mine. What this did was sow the majority of the seeds for PTSD that would manifest into tinnitus later on.

Even though I could communicate with my family and friends, the teachers would not encourage me to communicate verbally, and I was too young to realise that I had greater potential than they saw. Instead, I communicated by pointing to 'Makaton' signs on a board (a form of visual sign language). Communicating was frustrating since there was a limit to how much I could say. I learned to read the words underneath and did not concern myself with learning the many signs. They subsequently gave me a letter board where I pointed to letters to spell words, but even then, this was inadequate for how I wanted to communicate. This discouraged me from expressing emotions and feelings, and eventually, I trained myself to feel nothing. By this time, they had been trained not to surface consciously.

Gilligan reflects on the problem of shutting down emotionally,

> The caveat is that as life flows through you, it brings difficult or overwhelming experiences at times. So we have the capacity to shut down around the "tender soft spot", protecting it from damage. The problem, of course, is that shutting it down means that we are no longer connected to the pulse of life.[64]

I had turned into a ball of numbness as I engaged in school life, which entertained and occupied the minds of children with disabilities. This made it difficult to interact with the interpersonal world at school, and the longer this went on, the greater the damage to my sense of who I was as a person. This was because the environment of the special needs school was unnatural, which might explain why my response to it was also unnatural at a mental, physical and psychological level. Gilligan notes that Carl Jung, a Swiss psychiatrist, and psychoanalyst who founded analytical psychology, said that the subconscious attempts to compensate for the imbalance of the conscious by trying to bring balance. In addition, the subconscious attempts to bring wholeness by activating the complementary part, which will manifest as a negative symptom if treated negatively.[65]

Children with disabilities who could think for themselves, like me, had no autonomy over what happened to them. The teachers never found out that I could read and write, which I only learned extensively at seventeen when I went to a mainstream school.

In my experience, special needs environments suppress the natural abilities of children who are already vulnerable and need more physical assistance than your average child. Several reports suggested that I might have benefited from a more mainstream curriculum, but this was never followed through. Back then, special needs children were an aggravation, disrupting the status quo, and were to be barred from taking up precious resources from the mainstream.

When I was eight
now the time will come
they say to me as I crouch underneath them
and then they take me away to have a nice day
to spend time with them
but I don't want them
I want my parents
but now I'm in an institution made in hell
and here all kids are the same

but I'm not

and in vain

I cry out

let me out of here

I'm in prison

don't you see?

There are no walls around me

but they couldn't see the prison walls so high

they could nearly touch the sky

in my madness

I rushed to the gate

but it was locked

there was no debate

I wasn't a butterfly yet

I hadn't transformed on my own

my wings were still wet from the transformation

but I was half caterpillar

half hybrid in that institution made in hell

I wasn't well

my temperature went up to one hundred and three

now a caterpillar knows its own nature

and it knows its own destiny

and yet

it's trapped in the body of a cocoon

the shell that grew around it makes a natural prison

with prison guards standing at the gate allowing anyone in but nobody

out and so the caterpillar colony grew with butterflies that half died

but I was still alive

fully alive in fact

I couldn't crawl walk

fly or swim

for they thought I was dim from within

but I was a butterfly destined to be

but they destroyed my destiny

now I wonder when I would tell this tale again

I wonder when I will fly in the sky with my rainbow wings

rather than march to their marching tune in the afternoon of life

for a butterfly's work is never solemn and grey a butterfly's life is on the

wing to stay

like rainbows in the sky lighting it up with colour how many erasers does

it need to rub them out?

I'm not a pencil drawing

you cannot erase me from life just like that

for I drink honey nectar and not the sweet nectar poison

they gave me in a long ago land

in a long ago fairy-tale

where bridges were made of ice cream to melt away

so no man was an island

some would say

but the truth was forgotten by them

because rivers of ice cream would run down the lane

as reality melted away in the sunlight

to be replaced with circus clowns and pop up tents

clowns with extra white faces and extra broad smiles

grin from ear to ear but inside they were in fear

about what they had forgotten

those burning books

on the bookshelves of knowledge and wonder

but they were burning into hell

Creepy Teachers

When I was twelve, I was in a class with a male teacher who thought I was pretty. As I recollect, I often noticed him winking at and getting unusually close to some of the female teachers and pupils under the gaze of the headteacher. When he attempted the same with me, I did not react. Soon he left me alone and even talked to me respectfully. One day, he made a line drawing of me in my wheelchair. I wore a dark brown pair of trousers and a shirt that day, and he drew the picture in the same colour. There were breasts in his drawing, which embarrassed me. From what I remember, every time he drew a woman on the whiteboard, he would also draw breasts as if he was a bawdy teenager and not a man who ought to have assumed the responsibilities of a special needs teacher. In another similar instance, it was my birthday one year, and traditionally, parents would send a cake for their child to personally distribute around the school, offering a piece to members of staff. I did this one year, and three male teachers gathered around me; they took a slice of cake and simultaneously kissed me on my face. At the time, I thought this behaviour was commonplace, but upon reflection, it was far from appropriate. I had been trained not to consciously acknowledge my feeling of embarrassment (like many others). Some of the behaviour of the male teacher (mentioned above) was inappropriate, and he would have been more likely to be disciplined had he been a teacher at a mainstream school.

There was another teacher that, in my opinion, most children hated since he was strict and demanding. As I remember, he demonstrated authority by coming uncomfortably close to my face and talking slowly about what I needed to do. He slammed an open book shut in front of children's faces when they got something wrong or made a loud noise by dropping heavy hardback books or objects onto a table or the floor to make some children jump. I could not move away from the table because I was immobile in my wheelchair. Due to having Cerebral Palsy, I still maintain the Moro Reflex, which is a startle reflex usually lost during infancy; these sudden noises caused my legs to bruise when I hit them under the table. These are some examples of the many unpleasant memories of my years at the special needs school. I am aware that this book is about my recovery from tinnitus and not an autobiography, but I have added some recollections to provide context to my trauma.

No One Was Listening

At my special needs school, my emotions would surface consciously, but I would suppress them since I did not have the vocabulary to express them; I did not see the point either, as no one was interested enough to listen. Being born with a physical disability in a society that disdained disability, though not overtly, resulted in me learning not to respect or accept my emotional state or how I felt. I believed this was the right approach to take, but my subconscious needed respect, and my emotional state needed acknowledgement.

A couple of decades later, once I began hypnotherapy sessions, David Corr helped me understand the trauma of my past, which was when I realised that tinnitus was a manifestation of PTSD. Major adverse events in my childhood that I had no control over were also impossible to process and make sense of emotionally. As outlined earlier, this was the foundation of the tinnitus I later had as an adult. If intervention is not implemented, and if this is severe, prolonged or repeated without the proper support, this may result in PTSD. Gilligan describes how,

> "...conscious processes become self-contained in
> endless looping, thereby dissociating from

unconscious resources...this dissociation will be demonstrated by repetitive behavior in multiple channels – e.g., posture, verbal output, behavioral acts, images, accessed memories, ways of thinking."[66]

Gilligan further suggests that with the looping of the conscious, it loses the ability to be flexible and adaptable to changing situations in life and daily interactions; hence, the same undesirable results reoccur.[67]

Although this book is about my story of recovering from tinnitus, much of what I have written is also relevant to those with other symptoms of PTSD.

Men

I was uncomfortable around men as a child and later as a young woman. As I became a woman, I did not feel attractive; in fact, I felt disgusted with myself and did not feel worthy of womanhood. The experience of being with the teacher who drew a picture of me certainly had a significant role to play. I felt this way, partly because of my experience at school and partly because most men seemed to look through me as if I was not there. These unacknowledged emotions and feelings had nothing to do with my intelligence. In fact, my intelligence may have been why painful emotions did not surface consciously, stopping me from experiencing emotional pain in the moment. I later realised that it would have been normal to express my sadness, anger and frustration, but because of the conscious suppressing emotions from my subconscious, I did not feel them at all.

As an adult, Phil was the first genuine friend I had. We both belong to the Central London Humanist Group, where for once, I felt welcomed and respected. This is where I met Phil and some other friends (I explain how my friendship with Phil helped me feel comfortable around him on p. 135). I gradually grew in confidence as Phil helped me to realise that I was not different from other women. I face prejudice even today, but with Phil by my side, I know how to respond.

Not Processing Emotions

Even though I was disconnected from mainstream life as a girl, I knew I was intelligent and loved discovering things about the world. I survived at the very limits of my range, clinging on even in the conditions that did not suit me. My emotions and feelings went unacknowledged by adults, which meant that I learned not to process these at a conscious level, and this turned into tinnitus. To give an analogy, when we swallow food without chewing it, the food is too big to be digested by the gut and may remain lodged in the intestine. Over time, this could lead to digestion problems where food particles remain in the body and may build up unhealthily with nowhere to go. Similarly, if emotions go straight into the subconscious without being acknowledged and processed by the conscious, this could result in an emotional build-up of unacknowledged and unprocessed emotions in the subconscious. Through my hypnotherapy sessions, David helped me realise that one of the threads of tinnitus originated from my experience in the special needs school.

Minor events over time below conscious awareness if repeatedly left unacknowledged, preventing the retrieval of emotional information from the subconscious. When too many unprocessed emotions are completely unacknowledged, the overflow causes tinnitus.

David sometimes used a method called desensitisation, where I was encouraged to think about a traumatic event and to express my feelings and emotions towards it; at the same time, he provided me with a safe space to do so. He helped me to explore the reasons and the causes of my trauma while I reflected on how I felt. Sometimes this was done with the help of metaphors so that my subconscious could express itself. Due to not articulating my emotions and feelings for most of my life, I became accustomed to internalising them unhealthily. Through hypnosis, I learnt to retrieve emotions from the subconscious for the conscious to acknowledge. Once I achieved this, the tinnitus reduced in volume because hypnosis mostly works under conscious awareness. Yapko explains, "Practically speaking, some of what one experiences during hypnosis may not be recognized or retained in awareness; persons form responses outside of awareness, such as smiles or frowns in response to specific suggestions or internal experiences, such as memories, that arise."[68]

The point of full recovery is when all the emotions and feelings in the subconscious have been acknowledged consciously and when one can process emotional reactions immediately. This becomes possible when we can sort out emotions and feelings from the subconscious, like sorting household rubbish into paper, glass, metal, and plastic. The landfill of the subconscious needs to be reduced by the proper disposal of emotions. This was fundamental to my recovery from tinnitus. In an exercise that I describe on p. 301, the metaphor of clearing up from others that had fly-tipped on my property helped my subconscious to sort out and dispose of emotions that did not originate from me but were perceptions of myself given by others at a subconscious level. They became a part of how I saw myself as they slipped under the radar of my conscious awareness.

The Effect of Tinnitus on my Behaviour and Relationships

I am an extrovert by nature, and I enjoy spending time with friends. However, tinnitus dramatically affected my daily life and well-being; when it was loud, I found it difficult to have a conversation, and I became introverted. It was hard for me to have a sense of humour and handle tasks requiring concentration. In the initial stage of tinnitus, before my hypnotherapy sessions, I often felt a sense of dread; it felt as if I would not have much longer to live. I soon became accustomed to this and realised that if I did not have intervention in the form of treatment, I would be dead in the near future.

Contemplating Mortality

I often thought of my mortality, especially when the tinnitus was loud and the medical professionals had written me off. It was a beautiful day some summers after my diagnosis; my friends and I went walking in Epping forest. After our walk, I was lying on the grass with Phil. I could still hear the loud tinnitus while feeling happy about being amongst my friends. The sound had been extremely loud for ten days straight. I had been at this point many times, which made me consider my funeral arrangements. Phil is a humanist celebrant, and I asked him to conduct my funeral. Of course, he said no at first and assured me I would not die anytime soon, but I felt otherwise. He finally and reluctantly agreed. I was not afraid of death, but I was frightened of losing Phil and missing out on our love and friendship, as I thought I might not have long to live.

Friends And Family

My brother and nephew do not understand tinnitus or what I went through entirely. However, their attitude towards tinnitus was not the cause of stress as they were open and accepting of what I felt was real. They understood that my tinnitus would alter from hour to hour and affect me accordingly. I was going through a time in my life when I felt incredibly and overwhelmingly alone, even in the presence of others. Later on, my friends demonstrated that they did not understand what I was going through but were there to give me what I needed regardless. When I finally explained my experience to my friend Steve, he was surprised to learn that tinnitus felt more debilitating than Cerebral Palsy in some ways. In general, my friends did not offer pity or try to illustrate what I was feeling back to me as they knew they could not totally understand. This attitude helped me when I was feeling unwell with loud tinnitus. Friendship, as I recovered from tinnitus and particularly afterwards, is the most important thing I have in life. I hardly discussed what I was going through with my friends or anyone else except David and my psychotherapist. Nevertheless, my friends provided the emotional support and love that I needed. This, in turn, helped me learn that opening up to someone else was not necessarily bad.

My Nephew

Before and during my hypnotherapy sessions, my young nephew would stay over. During school holidays and weekends, I would spend time with him, taking him out or doing projects at home that he enjoyed. Ever since he was young, he has loved baking cakes and cookies. Even though I was unable to assist him physically, he enjoyed the fact that I was with him. My personal assistant would turn on the oven and do other physical tasks that I could not do so we could bake together. He and I love animals, and it was in the Easter holidays one year that I took him on a surprise visit to a children's farm. He enjoyed petting and feeding the animals, and I could just be like any other aunt; a caregiver, a responsible adult, and someone my nephew had fun with, without the  limitations of my disability. On these days, my tinnitus would either go down to a low level where I could just about hear it or not be there at all. His profound effect on my tinnitus could have been because he was too young to have emotional baggage. Instead, he had a cheerful and playful persona created by most children's innocent and happy emotions. In effect, this was the converse to being in the presence of those with emotional baggage. As a child, I learnt to guard against supposedly wrong thoughts and emotions. This was because of what other people had subtly implied during their interactions with me, and this formed a part of the barrier between the subconscious and the conscious.

Impaired Memory

I appeared normal to the outside world, but on the inside, I was being tortured from moment to moment, so naturally, others were less understanding of what I was going through. The act of being alive was a challenge. My short-term memory was severely affected for a few years. Without realising it, I would have the same conversation with the same people over a short time span. In our daily conversations, we collect things that others have said and done and then form an appropriate response. I could not remember what I had said or done, which is why my responses to other people were flawed. I would forget instructions given to me within a few minutes. This led to people becoming frustrated and angry about my incompetence, again leading to my tinnitus becoming louder, followed by the onset of depression. I had lost the ability to be responsible for myself since memory is our first line of defence in an interaction. Jerome Kagan, psychologist and author of *An Argument for Mind,* wrote:

> "Nothing about human thought, feeling and behaviour can be understood without acknowledging that humans evaluate events, others and themselves on a good-bad continuum and try to acquire the personal features they judge as praiseworthy."[69]

It is usual for most people to have random and unconstrained thoughts where one thought often follows another, even though the connection between the two might be extremely flimsy. Eric Klinger et al. commented that "...task unrelated thoughts (TUTs) ...One key theory is that imaginative TUTs function to remind us of our personal concerns, including our unresolved problems and future goals...".[70] In my case, thoughts that followed were prevented from surfacing consciously because of the neuromuscular lock.

By stifling emotions that were uncomfortable or at odds with how others saw me, the conscious effectively policed the subconscious. I reined in both deliberate and automatic thoughts, making it less likely for unpremeditated thoughts to come to the conscious; this was when the conscious imposed control over what surfaced from my subconscious. This was when my thoughts were likely to be lasting, regular and unable to move easily from one topic to another. Through my hypnotherapy sessions, I learned to acknowledge my emotions while not allowing other people to affect how I felt; the denial of my emotions would make the tinnitus louder.

Stress And My Imaginary Bubble

One effect of tinnitus was that the sound would become louder if there was stress in the immediate environment, even if it was not directed at me. For example, a quarrel in another room could increase the volume in my ear. This was because the barrier that shielded me from other people's unpleasant feelings would vanish, leaving me vulnerable and exposed to those in my immediate surroundings; this is another example of a Neuromuscular Lock (explained earlier on p. 72). This contributed to the emotional backlog already overflowing in my subconscious. In the past, trauma was recognised as solely a physical issue. Later on, it was also understood to have psychological impacts, which was when it became apparent that this resulted from a punctured mental defence.[71] Through hypnosis, I learned to imagine that there was a beautiful pink bubble encasing me that protected me from external negative emotions (also see p. 319). This is how I built a protective mechanism via my conscious imagination to prevent other people's emotions from spilling onto me. Since I also imagined that this was a bubble with intelligence, I trusted it to know which emotions to keep out and which to let in (also see Point of Light exercise on p. 311). This indicates that hypnosis is a self-repair practise.

Part B - Insights on Trauma

Post-traumatic stress disorder (PTSD) was first recognised in 1980, initially conceived by the American Psychiatric Association. It standardised the formula for behaviour and support with a common language and a method to classify behavioural issues after traumatic events. Treatments and measurements of PTSD vary from one practitioner to another.[72] Trauma is not exclusive to war veterans or those involved in road traffic accidents; its forms are subtler. It has been understood for a long while that trauma can cause long-term physiological and psychological issues, as in my case.[73] Gerald Young is a Full Professor in Psychology at Glendon College, York University, Toronto, Canada. He found that what may be traumatic to one person may be ordinary to another. There are millions of children around the world with disabilities who attend special needs schools, but not all experience PTSD as I have; in fact, only a minority experiencing trauma will develop chronic PTSD.[74] I am reminded of the saying by the Roman poet and philosopher Titus Lucretius Carus, "One man's medicine is another man's poison". It was probably the case of me having a greater awareness of myself as an emotional and intellectual child in my special needs school. In contrast, the majority of other children there appeared satisfied. Trauma was a part of my everyday reality, and I grew to realise this while being powerless to do anything about it.

According to Lori A. Zoellner and Joyce N. Bittinger, researchers at the Department of Psychology, University of Washington, often when trauma survivors tell of their experiences with trauma, memories become fragmented and confusing regarding the sequence of events. For example, the sound and imagery of the event may appear vividly yet be fragmented and incomplete. This becomes a disassociated memory that is never rehearsed, making it difficult for the person to recall the traumatic event in the order it was experienced.[75] This is because Arnaud D'Argembeau, professor at the University of Liège, makes the connection between memory and the sense of identity,

> "This self-directed mentalizing process may help us make meaning out of our experiences, further cementing our sense of identity and contributing to the development of self-schemas, stable traits that form the basis of our personality."[76]

These memories cannot contribute to one's self-identity over time, where specific elements of past events are typically combined with our "autobiographical knowledge base." Traumatic memories become isolated, where fragments fade with time. It is argued that the fading of memory makes it impossible to retrieve, even with hypnosis. However, my experience of this differs. Hypnosis, Automatic Writing, and the Dream Analysis method (explained later) have proved fruitful. I have always been able to remember what happened vividly at my special needs school. Still, I had lost the ability to bring up the associated feelings and emotions of that time, which is why these were incomplete events. In the case of trauma, this association is broken, which is why trauma survivors often find it challenging to remember events in their entirety.[77] The aim of treatment is the ability to recall the sequence of events in the order they occurred.[78] One school of thought suggests that in conventional memory recollection, the recall of a particular memory is followed by the recollection of other associated memories.

One year, I received a Christmas e-card from an acquaintance. The e-card had an animation of the journey of Mary and Joseph with the donkey to Bethlehem, and the carol that accompanied this was Little Donkey, which I had not heard for many years. Upon hearing it, I felt complete disgust. Realising this was not a normal reaction, I listened to it again. I was immediately reminded of the nativity play that I was a part of each year in my special needs school which brought up other associated memories. Dorthe Berntsen and Anne Staerk Jacobsen, who have undertaken research into mental time travel, observe that "Mental time travel can occur both deliberately – for example, one can deliberately try to recall a conversation and replay it in one's mind – and involuntarily, as in the example of experiencing a memory triggered by hearing an old song on the radio...".[79] It is essential to take the time to realise why we feel the way we do about specific experiences, even if they are minor. I continue to do this even though this is not necessary. When I used to have tinnitus, this would often bring it down. If an experience provokes a strong reaction, but you are unable to identify the reason or the source, I would recommend directly asking the subconscious through Automatic Writing, a method for the subconscious to express itself through the written form outlined in Chapter 9. Alternatively, the Focusing method, which enables you to tap into your subconscious, is another effective way, which I describe in Chapter 12.

In a study by Juliane Sachschal *et al.*, 2019 of the Department of Experimental Psychology (University of Oxford), she observed that memory disjointedness was more common in those who were exposed to a traumatic film but had no history of PTSD.[80] The authors' theory suggests that it becomes possible to recall the entire set of associated memories when the first is remembered.[81] Emotions and sensations act as cues to bring up the memory in a particular schema.[82] For example, if a person experienced some kind of abuse, and the abuser used a particular perfume or cologne, when the person happens to smell the same scent, they may simultaneously recall the abuse since the smell becomes a cue. One theory by Bessel van der Kolk, MD, who has spent his professional life studying how children and adults adapt to traumatic experiences, suggests that trauma is divided from memory, the two wholly dissociated from each other. The result is that the conscious cannot organise and make sense of the trauma in its entirety. This may result in PTSD. He further explains that traumatic events are not altered by other, perhaps more pleasant events or with the passage of time.[83]

Chapter 7

The Importance of Acknowledging my Subconscious

It is essential to acknowledge what the subconscious says, and persistence is vital in this endeavour. My tinnitus was a form of Post-Traumatic Stress Disorder (PTSD); it was necessary to explore my childhood trauma to recover from it. This process changed me for the better; as a result, I have different priorities in life. My relationships with those I care about are more profound, with greater quality and meaning. I will explain how understanding myself and my relationship with the past was vital for recovery and how it helped me deal with the emotional backlog which resulted in tinnitus. Here, I also outline the effect of finding David Corr, my hypnotherapist, and how, with his help, I learnt to reconnect with emotions. I will demonstrate the importance of being committed to daily treatment of tinnitus and how hypnosis became a way of life for me rather than a prescribed set of activities. This chapter finally lays out the process of building a relationship between the subconscious and the conscious, facilitating the communication between my two identities, which eventually became one.

Post-Traumatic Stress Disorder

When a person is exposed to a situation outside the normal range of human experience that would be distressing to virtually anyone, PTSD is a natural human response to an atypical situation.[84]

PTSD can happen to anyone at any age, resulting from natural or manmade events that they find highly distressing. These include, but are not limited to: domestic violence, sexual abuse, being held prisoner, major accidents, terrorist attacks and various forms of trauma.[85] Gilligan points out that,

> "Researchers such as Peter Levine (1997, 2010) and Robert Sapolsky (1998) have described how virtually all mammals respond to severe life threats with what I call a *trauma trance,* a paradoxical state of body immobilization accompanied by high internal arousal. While such a trauma trance lasts only a short period in most mammals, releasing once the threat recedes, humans (and animals conditioned by humans) can stay in it indefinitely – years, decades, even generations. In such states of neuromuscular lock, consciousness is restricted to recreating the same experience over and over again."[86]

When my conscious suppressed the emotions associated with having a disability and my experiences at the special needs school, my conscious and the subconscious began to disconnect. The conscious put up a barrier between it and the subconscious (see p. 169) so that I would stop feeling anything at all in the moment, and then, numbness set in.

As Edna B. Foa et al., Professor of Clinical Psychology in Psychiatry at the University of Pennsylvania suggests,"...the clinical picture for trauma survivors is often complicated by associated features, such as guilt, dissociation, alterations in personality, affect dysregulation, and marked impairment in intimacy and attachment..."[87]

Emeritus Prof. Fred Alford of the University of Maryland, who researches the experience of trauma, observes that "From the perspective of PTSD, trauma causes psychological injury that results in depression, social alienation, and withdrawal."[88] There may also be physical ailments such as pain, sweating, feeling sick or trembling, headaches, dizziness, chest pains or stomach aches. This is one example of how mental and emotional states can manifest into physiological symptoms.

The Regime

After I entered the special needs system as a young girl, I was on the verge of having little or no emotions at my disposal. Even though there was no structure to education in my special needs school, the day had a strict routine. For example, there were two "lessons" before lunch, with a break in between where the staff put out orange squash for the children in plastic beakers with names written on masking tape. At midday, the main hall was turned into a dining area. The children who could feed themselves sat here while those like myself who needed to be fed were relegated to a classroom. I still cannot understand why there was such segregation in a school where children were already segregated from their able-bodied peers. The woman who fed me was in her fifties and was from the local Sikh community. She sat in front of me and said, "Open your mouth", whenever she wanted to shove another mouthful in. I refused out of stubbornness since I knew when I needed another mouthful. After lunch, I went to the bathroom, and we had two more "lessons" after that. Shortly before three, I saw the council buses pulling up in the playground, ready to take us home. The tail lift took my wheelchair into the bus, after which the escort bolted it to the floor using two clamps, a metaphor for my present life. It was a time in my life with little emotional substance and an imposed regime. This is one example where my conscious was encouraged to endlessly loop because of the strict daily structure that was instilled. Keeping special needs children mindlessly occupied had been a common practice for decades. There was an incentive for special needs schools to look after these children and keep them away from mainstream society; I recognised a bleak future. This was the fracture point that engendered my tinnitus later on. I understood the gravity of my situation, but as a young girl, I was powerless to initiate change.

What I got out of life then was a mystery in my colourless world
I became a robot just like the special needs system had wanted me to
we all marched to the tune of the special needs drum beat
but a flame flickered inside behind closed eyelids undamaged
undamped by the loveless atmosphere
it burnt on
but that flame was so small
I didn't think love existed at all

With my emotions receding into the subconscious, I lost access to them. If my conscious could have articulated, it would have said, "Never again will I feel so much pain as my circumstances have caused me to now." The result was that I became a robotic child in a wheelchair, and numbness set in. Inside, though, my subconscious rebelled. I just could not hear it. It needed me to have a mainstream life and to grow, play and learn like other children who became familiar with their emotional landscape, learning to pick out the right emotions for the appropriate response. If I had gone to a mainstream school straight after nursery, the cost of providing me with exclusive transport and one-to-one support would have been beyond the realms of possibility. After all, I would never have been able to repay it back into the economy due to being unable to work. So clearing up mainstream society and taking the burden off mainstream schools appeared to be the main objective for the council.

The tinnitus that I developed was the way PTSD expressed itself. One explanation for tinnitus is that I had become successful at ignoring the less intrusive symptoms while continuing with daily life. Bessel A. Van der Kolk writes, "Traumatic memories come back as emotional and sensory states with little verbal representation. This failure to process information on a symbolic level, which is essential for proper categorization and integration with other experience, is at the very core of the pathology of PTSD."[89] Only through my hypnotherapy sessions did I learn that the noise was the build-up of unprocessed emotions in the subconscious, which needed to be acknowledged by the conscious. I now know that tinnitus's intrusive and disturbing nature was the only way the subconscious could have got my attention to indicate something was terribly wrong.

Trauma

For those who have survived trauma, PTSD is a complex route to navigate. Every strand of regular functioning can be impaired in the most severe forms. According to Foa et al., "Posttraumatic stress disorder (PTSD) is a complex, often chronic and debilitating mental disorder that develops in response to catastrophic life events such as combat, sexual assault, natural disasters, and other extreme stressors."[90]

War veterans who have experienced or witnessed distressing events in their careers are the first thought that comes to mind when considering PTSD. However, I had survived the special needs system after being born with a disability. For my entire life, until I met David, I did not acknowledge how the relationship between my disability and the negative perception of others, such as those in my special needs school, impacted me emotionally. I resorted to any lengths to prevent myself from being reminded of this painful period in my life, for example, by not engaging in a conversation about these topics or not revisiting places that triggered unwanted memories.

An Education

At the ripe old age of seventeen, I finally became a fourth-year pupil in a mainstream school. I decided never to discuss my special needs school as I wore my navy uniform and crisp white shirt every day to attend my new school. With hard work, determination and self-discipline, I learned the basics of maths and how to read and write. I was a silent witness to my developing intellect. Even though it was the first time I had to wear a uniform and follow the rules, I found something to laugh about with my friends and personal assistants. Life was marvellous since my special needs school was a memory. For once, I had excellent and supportive teachers, even though they were aware of my lack of knowledge and had little experience dealing with someone with a disability. As a pupil in the fourth year, I was unsure whether my new teachers had confidence in my ability to obtain my GCSEs since my lack of education was very apparent. The most striking thing about them was that they did not show their anxiety if they had any. After a few months, I managed to cope with the work and began understanding what was being taught. I felt wonderful and free, even though I had lots of homework each night. The harder I worked, the more I improved. I was given a computer with specialised software and hardware, which I accessed by hitting a switch with my left hand to type. Even though it was physically tiring, it helped to demonstrate that I was completing the work myself. This gave the teachers confidence in me as a pupil that had not come from a mainstream background. The work became interesting and stimulating as I began to understand what was required.

Once, we did a project in geography about noise pollution in the environment; I presented my project in the form of a poster on a green card. A few weeks after handing this in, I was surprised and delighted to see it on the wall of one of the corridors in the geography block. My history lessons were engaging too. We learned about the Vietnam War, the South African apartheid and Indian independence from the British Raj. I also enjoyed my English lessons; we studied First World War poets like Rupert Brook, Wilfred Owen and Isaac Rosenberg. I was introduced to 1984 by George Orwell and the Diary Of Anne Frank, both of which were thoroughly engaging.

In contrast, only a few months prior, my teacher in my special needs school would ask me questions that a primary school teacher may have asked. On one occasion, he had asked me to name the prime minister of England at the time; I crumbled inside as if something had broken. I was shocked and could not speak since this said everything about how much the special needs school had suppressed me. I finally responded by giving him the name of the prime minister of India, I knew it was a ridiculous answer, but I wanted to see his reaction. As I expected, he said without showing surprise that the answer was wrong when I was hoping that he would realise that the correct answer was so obvious that he should not have asked me. When I began hypnotherapy, I developed the Whispering Exercise explained on p. 274. I undertook this exercise where I visualised the same classroom scene but this time imagining

David whispering in my ear. This helped me to overcome the emotional trauma, even though it was decades later. In a study by Emily Holmes et al. 2016, a Clinical Psychologist with a Ph.D. in Cognitive Neuroscience, her research demonstrates that the vividness of the way we imagine a scene from the past does not correlate to how depressed we are.[91] This is important in hypnosis and the treatment of trauma when we are likely to revisit past traumatic memories. This is where the Whispering Exercise provides a possible solution; the subconscious brings up traumatic memories, but these are infiltrated positively to make the trauma less potent while avoiding denial.

Attempting Without Knowing

The first lesson I attended on one Monday in October 1990 at my mainstream school was with Mr Smith. He was a short man with a handlebar moustache and a broad smile who might have been in his late fifties. Mr Smith was one of the kindest people I have ever met. When I first began my education with him, my situation was hopeless. I attempted to do maths at GCSE level when I did not know simple arithmetic. He explained the methods of finding the area of a triangle. I stared incomprehensibly at the whiteboard; I did not understand a single thing. He may as well have been talking in some foreign language. Panic began to grow inside me; it was a moment I will not forget; the floor refused to open up and swallow me as I wanted. Finally, Mr Smith decided that Peter, my personal assistant, would try to teach me. I saw a different attitude in Peter when we left class and went to the library. There, I had no choice but to explain my special needs school. He was sympathetic and felt I was thrown into a complex situation. Peter said he would do his best to educate me, and in turn, I felt sorry for this man who was given the responsibility of becoming my personal assistant but had more to do than he had bargained for. I felt numb and shocked, but I soon realised that there was someone to help me escape the abyss I was in. Due to these unusually demanding circumstances, I had no time or resources to reflect on the past because I was attempting to secure a positive future, and I had much catching up to do.

A Gentle Way

As the threat of remaining institutionalised for life was gone, there was a deeper sense of release and hope for the future. Something gentler, more harmonious, seemed to be stirring into life. I was not frustrated for the first time and looked forward to the days ahead. There was so much to learn, so much to do, and so many fights to watch in the playground. I left behind the memories of the special needs school, locking them in a box somewhere in my subconscious. I now had no time for them since I was satisfied with my new, mainstream life and friends with mainstream stories to tell.

I made a very good friend in school; Rebecca was two years younger than me. She would push my wheelchair down the corridor and shout, "Boot the door", which notified those who happened to be behind the big double fire doors that we were coming along the way to our classroom. At this point, I straightened both my legs, taking aim, and then the doors swung open, crashing into the walls behind them; we had just enough time to make it through. This was incredibly entertaining and the only way we could navigate the school in my wheelchair. She mentioned she had been bullied before my time, which stopped soon after my arrival because she chose to spend all her time with me. I was surprised, but she went on to tell me that our teachers had informed her parents of her improved attendance, which she attributed to my arrival. This was because she knew I was relying on her to help me get around, and she was the only person, apart from my personal assistant, who could understand my speech and help me communicate in class. We spent most of the time laughing and cracking jokes, sometimes about others. This was one advantage of having a speech impairment that only she understood.

For decades I considered my history too problematic and painful to recollect. After my traumatic experience of being confined in the special needs system, it would have been normal to recall memories repeatedly or feel on edge or anxious. However, I ensured that the past did not pollute the present. I felt human and alive while the experience at my special needs school faded into my subconscious.

The Turning Point

The very important relationship between hypnotherapist and client must benefit both in a goal-directed fashion. Hypnosis cannot be achieved by fixed and rigid techniques that are used on everyone. Instead, therapeutic relationships need to adapt to the requirements of the individual. According to Gilligan, "The complexity of human behaviour and its underlying motivations makes necessary a cognizance of the multitude of factors existing in any situation arising between two personalities engaged in a joint activity." [92]

One afternoon in January 2010, I arrived at a shop near Waterloo station, went inside, and the woman behind the counter smiled as I inquired after David Corr. She led me to a small room behind the shop and knocked on the door. A thin, smartly dressed man with white hair appeared. He smiled as he introduced himself and invited me in. The room was warm and comfortable, with a relaxing aroma of lavender. There were two chairs, one on each side of the table. He sat opposite me and welcomed me to my first appointment. Unlike other professionals, David asked about the kind of noise I was experiencing, where it was and how it made me feel. After our formal introductions and making me feel comfortable and welcomed, he wanted to know everything about the noise, asking me to describe it as vividly as possible. At this point, his manner of speaking became slower and the sentences shorter; this was my first experience of trance.

I came up with a colour, shape, and description of an image that fitted the sound. It was that of a sparkly red ball. What David had done was cue my subconscious to prepare it for an instruction to follow. Erickson taught us that we are more receptive to messages learning and change in the trance state.[93] I felt absorbed by David's voice and words - I was no longer aware of any other reality. He then asked what I would like to do with this sparkly red ball. My response seemed to come from a place that I did not recognise; as I said, I would like to put it out in the cool rain. David asked me to imagine this sparkly red ball in the cool rain, repeating my words to notice what happened (this exercise is outlined on p. 310). At this point, my tinnitus decreased slightly, which gave me reason to believe that I was on the verge of something incredible. I caught my first glimpse into hypnosis and the genius before me.

The abilities and power of the imagination should not be underestimated. It allowed me to think of something unreal in the physical world, but I had given it three-dimensional form in the spatiotemporal world. Through the subconscious, I had given the tinnitus a physical form I could manipulate and gain some control over. Yapko explains further about hypnosis, "The hypnotic state, in this view, is created by the hypnotic induction process, which presumably alters the person's consciousness through the narrowing of attention to the offered suggestions."[94] It was a beginning, a new way of thinking, a spark that, ultimately, triggered a sweeping chain reaction that continues to this day. My decision to begin this journey of repair and discovery into the subconscious would, within a matter of days, would begin to change everything. As with all such pivotal moments, David was the key.

David gained my trust, and I felt the beginnings of a good rapport with him. These were the right conditions to obtain trance responses. To my amazement, the tinnitus went down slightly. Anna Abraham is a Professor in Creativity and Gifted Education at the University of Georgia, Athens, who notes that, "Our imaginations render it possible to fabricate alternative realities and fictional realms that we have never experienced in quite the same manner before."[95] The human imagination is vast and allows us to evoke images, impressions, emotions, and ideas at will. The enormous space it inhabits allows us to consider the plausible and the implausible, the real and the fictional. The imagination is unconstrained and intentional while inhabiting the conscious and subconscious realms.[96] In my experience, the imagination plays a pivotal role in hypnosis.

I always have had a vivid imagination that I had not previously thought would come to my aid. However, a few minutes into my first hypnotherapy session, I realised that my imagination was an extraordinarily powerful tool when combined with applied hypnosis. Hypnosis relies on the imagination in a goal-directed fashion, though not entirely. While the imagination depends on the possibilities of a hypothesis that could be true, with hypnosis, anything becomes possible, making it effective in emotional and psychological recovery. This is where the imagination diverges from hypnosis, even though the latter relies on the former. Over the years, hypnosis continues to improve my well-being, growth and resilience, providing confidence that the tinnitus will not return. "The capacity to perceive such change is called post-traumatic *growth*."[97]

David had been trained in the Ericksonian hypnotherapy technique, defined by Gilligan as "...descriptions of Ericksonian trances frequently emphasize feelings of being acknowledged and safely encouraged to explore an inner self, pleasant surprises and enhanced feelings of selfesteem, competency, and self-acceptance."[98]

On hypnosis, Yapko writes that, "Therapy is organized around the belief that people can discover and develop the very resources within themselves that they need."[99] I would later discover this in my hypnotherapy sessions, which would prove invaluable to my recovery. Had I met David in my childhood, I doubt I would have had tinnitus in the first place since he would have taught me how to stay connected with my emotions despite experiencing trauma, but there is no point in regretting what happened or failed to happen in the past. As an adult, I was in his presence, which was all that mattered. Even though recovering from tinnitus is my journey, the relationship between David and I, therapist and client, is very special to me. It was important to have someone who did not believe I was crazy and acknowledged me as a sufferer and eventually a recoverer of tinnitus. Within the first session, my persistent migraine disappeared, and the constant noise went down ever so slightly. I soon began to view David as a teacher, and I still have the utmost respect for him and the knowledge, time, and energy he gave me with every session.

A common misconception about hypnosis is that it is a form of mind control where the hypnotist has the ability to make you do what they want. I learned that hypnosis was far from relinquishing control to another person. Yapko highlights this point, "All individuals are as psychologically safe as they want, need, or choose to be. If someone wants to reject suggestions, no matter how deeply absorbed in hypnosis, the ability to do so is retained. A "deeper" hypnotic experience doesn't increase compliance. The defences someone can employ are both conscious and unconscious, so even suggestions that escape conscious scrutiny can still encounter unconscious defenses."[100] I hope this proves sufficient for those who might be sceptical about hypnosis, but may wish to try it.

Having David Corr as my hypnotherapist was the best experience I have had. His immense knowledge about how the subconscious functions and his exquisite understanding of tinnitus was a fantastic combination to have in a therapist. Indeed, I have felt humbled in his presence, and I am fortunate to have found such an ordinary genius. Though he denies his power, the process of recovery would have been impossible without him. I owe my life to my co-creator, the most amazing teacher and being, the phenomenon that is David Corr.

My regular hypnotherapy sessions with David were a lifeline to survival, and often I would exist from one session to another since the tinnitus would go down after every session with the hypnotherapy exercises, but would go up in a few days that followed. Over time, I learned the principles and practices I was taught by David and would practise them daily, improving my approach to these exercises. In addition, I took a notebook and pen to every session for my personal assistant to make notes on what he had taught me. This knowledge was vitally important since I would put his advice into daily practice.

Approximately two months after beginning my hypnotherapy sessions with David, I had several exercises at my disposal. I had managed to develop the ability to bring the tinnitus to a lower level using hypnosis. I began to feel happy and hopeful about the future as the tinnitus decreased slowly, but definitely. I finally had a real possibility of making a full recovery.

A Therapist Is Not A Cure, But The Subconscious Is

Later, David said he had learned much from me about taking responsibility and control over my condition. The homework he set was immensely useful in between sessions, where I could often reduce the volume of tinnitus by myself, empowering me. I would also research the methods that David had taught me and consider how I could refine them. Experimentation was an essential part of what I did in between sessions, where I often discovered new techniques based on the principles of hypnosis for treating tinnitus. The chapter on Dream Analysis and Automatic Writing describes just two of the practices I developed independently of David whilst discussing these practices with him during the sessions to get his perspective. This was extremely useful in developing and refining methods.

I understand from David that some clients complained about being given homework since they believed that a paid therapist was responsible for "curing" them. This was the wrong approach to take with hypnosis. After all, each person is responsible for their mental health, and therapists are there to offer guidance, support and learning. Hypnosis is fundamentally a way of living where one must constantly ensure that the subconscious is being acknowledged, which is impossible for a therapist to do for you. Alan Bryman, Professor of Organisational and Social Research at the University of Leicester, explains the importance of being resourceful,

> "It seems to me that the only way you can begin to get close to the kind of methods that are reliable in natural scientific or engineering work is to use every tool you've got. You know, our tools are so inadequate and the material to which we're applying them is so slippery that you've got to use

everything you have."[101]

The conscious can support the subconscious in expressing itself, which is fundamental to self-hypnosis. Eisen and Yapko argue that,

> "The conscious ultimately decides what is possible to do and what is not possible to do, although such decisions may well be-and usually are-based on influences from past experiences, cognitive styles, or personality dynamics that are largely unconscious."[102]

Having studied hypnosis for many years, I have attempted to reverse this, making my subconscious the dominant decision-maker. Throughout and after my recovery, an exercise I regularly engage with is Automatic Writing, using the Roads and Roundabouts exercise on p. 173. Through this exercise, my subconscious communicates clearly and unambiguously to the conscious. This could be useful advice about something I am unsure about or instructions directly from the subconscious. This ensures that I acknowledge the subconscious and actively perform the task it wants. This could be a form of Automatic Writing, a hypnosis exercise, or an activity I need to undertake. If the latter is the case, my subconscious often provides specific instructions on what I need to do and how I need to do the activity, along with an explanation of why it is beneficial. I see it not as a form of bondage but as a way of the conscious remaining in touch with the subconscious and for me to experience life in line with what is suitable and beneficial for me emotionally. I implicitly trust my subconscious because I have learned that it has my best interests at heart.

It is possible to automatically write anywhere while not necessarily writing it down. It is a way of quickly seeking advice from the subconscious, especially when I am unsure about what to do. This is also useful when I may know what to do but want a second opinion, and in this way, I keep connected with my subconscious. It is like having an invisible conjoined twin that is always looking out for me and is wiser than I am. It is important to be creative regularly, allowing the subconscious to express itself in other forms, such as painting, drawing, making music, or arts and crafts. It is unnecessary to produce a masterpiece or have any art skills. Being creative is enough since it may give the subconscious a form of expression. Due to having a physical disability, I am unable to use my hands, so I verbalise Automatic Writing for another person to write down verbatim, or I use a specialised computer that I can access independently. This is a suitable method for my subconscious to express itself.

For me, hypnotherapy is a way of life and not a set of exercises administered by a therapist; it does not work like that. Even after recovering from tinnitus, I remain consistently in love, fascinated and curious about what possibilities hypnotherapy opens up in the way I understand my subconscious. I feel like an enthusiastic child relying on an adult (my subconscious) to teach me something new daily. This helps me to be patient, open and respectful. I have learnt to accept this knowledge to be true no matter how painful or disturbing it might be to what I understand at a conscious level.

A Useful Scale to Measure Tinnitus

Tinnitus was a form of torture and even though I was in agony, I was unable to see or feel what part of my body was being tortured or who or what was torturing me. Although this is a metaphorical analogy of the pain that I felt, it is hard to describe it in a better way. However, Gilligan

123

eloquently expresses this type of pain, "This pain marks the spot and reveals the presence of the center. It may not have words; it may not have any acknowledgement at all, but it exists."[103] Gilligan suggests it is wiser to attend to this pain rather than ignore it. During my hypnotherapy sessions and work outside, I tended to deflect attention away from the pain, perhaps a coping strategy of the conscious. I often needed to articulate to David how loud in volume my tinnitus was. He taught me to describe the volume as a number between 0 and 10, where 0 was no tinnitus at all and 10 was loud enough to make me faint, which I once did. I needed to get some exercise, and I stood in my standing frame; after a few minutes, I blacked out. The tinnitus was louder than a jet engine and excruciatingly painful, but not in a sensory way typically associated with physical pain. This scale helped me to define the volume of tinnitus to David, and later on, it became useful in my practice to assess whether a hypnosis exercise was working or not and to what extent. David also helped me describe the noise in a language we could both understand and work with. For me, the sound of tinnitus was white noise or static, but other people hear it differently. It is virtually impossible to describe tinnitus to someone who has never experienced it. Through hypnosis, I learnt to pay attention to what the pain was telling me. Gilligan suggests that we ignore our centre, because our past experiences have taught us that this is the correct way of doing things.

The Utilisation of Personal Experience

Nearly everything we do in our daily lives can be turned into a metaphor for emotional recovery, which is one way that hypnosis can be lived. Upon understanding this, I developed a method of using metaphors to define objects and people (discussed further in the Dream Analysis chapter). Once these metaphors and their emotional definitions were established as a common language between my subconscious and conscious, it was possible to create therapeutic experiences utilising my daily activities. Hypnosis in everyday life became an interactive emotional experience where the objects and experiences in my physical environment were enhanced by the generated emotional information from my subconscious. This happened across multiple sensory modalities, including visual, auditory, haptic (the ability to manipulate objects using touch and proprioception), somatosensory (the ability to sense pain, pressure and heat in the body, its location and the intensity) and olfactory (relating to the sense of smell).

Grinder et al. explain how Erickson used the principle of utilisation in his therapeutic practice,

> "Erickson seizes upon the information offered by the client as to which portion of the world of ongoing experience is available to them and utilizes the representational system information by directing their attention to experiences within that representational system but outside of the client's present awareness."[104]

Utilisation became a vital part of my lifestyle, where it was impossible to distinguish therapy from daily life, one integrated into the other. This enabled the subconscious and the conscious to maintain connection and foster communication. More importantly, it provided opportunities for the tinnitus to go down. I describe how I used dream metaphors to encourage a repairing process in wakefulness at the end of the Dream Analysis Chapter on p. 259. Later in my recovery, I developed a dream analysis method that was efficient in reducing tinnitus on a daily basis.

Utilisation

It is crucial that I am comfortable with whatever metaphors I use in utilisation. For example, due to my physical disability, my right hand has minimal function, but my left hand has about fifty per cent of normal function. This means I am left-handed, and my left hand is also the most dexterous part of my body. When this is turned into a metaphor, this can be interpreted as the subconscious being the most emotionally dexterous part of me because it has the most wisdom and it is able to manipulate the emotional world. Based on this principle, I turn the tinnitus into an object; for example, I can imagine the tinnitus is a red ball. I imagine this ball travelling from my ear down through my left shoulder, into my arm, into my hand and finally out in my left palm. I open and close my left hand at will, which sends a message to the tinnitus that my left hand (my subconscious) is in control of it. At this point, the tinnitus often goes down. In this way, I utilise the ability of my left hand, but I invite the reader to find their own method of utilisation with a metaphor that they are comfortable with. This is one example of how I did not limit hypnosis to a hypnotherapy session but carried the principles of hypnosis throughout my day and integrated it into my daily life.

I now effectively integrate life into hypnosis, ensuring the subconscious and conscious maintain connection and communication. I invite the reader to consider what experiences in their daily life that they can draw upon as a form of utilisation.

I have always been fascinated at how a caterpillar that is limited to living on the ground eventually becomes a creature with the ability to fly; its transformation into a butterfly is natural and irreversible. I associate this metaphor with going from the state of once having tinnitus to experiencing silence. This is why I try to use butterfly imagery wherever I can in my daily life. For example, I have a duvet cover and a pillow with butterfly imagery. The outfit I wore to celebrate my recovery (see the Epilogue on p. 330) was a white dress with butterflies. The time that I wore a dress prior to this was when I went to school, which is why I was slightly surprised when my subconscious had chosen the dress for me and insisted that I purchase it and wear it on this occasion. Phil gave me a blanket and wall stickers with butterflies on them. The wall stickers now decorate the wardrobe door in my bedroom. He also gave me a beautiful butterfly bracelet I wear on special occasions. He and Lucy, my friend and Phil's wife, are the only people who know how much I like butterflies. Lucy painted a picture of a pink and gold butterfly which is on the wall where I write. Surrounding myself with images of butterflies was a subtle way of reminding the subconscious of its important task of transforming into something it is meant to become. Now the mission of the butterfly imagery is to remind the subconscious to remain in its transformed state.

Chapter 8

My Subconscious Expressing Itself Through the Written Word

My emotional backlog resulted in post-traumatic stress disorder and tinnitus. I learned to deal with it once hypnosis established a relationship between my conscious and subconscious. So it was a significant and unpleasant surprise when, through my sessions with David, I realised that my tinnitus resulted from emotional trauma, most of which stemmed from my childhood and the ramifications of physical disability. At that point, I had the option of walking away from David and his hypnotherapy sessions to avoid engaging with the painful and uncomfortable emotions associated with the past, but I decided that getting back the silence I once had was my only priority.

As a *Doctor Who* fan, I found this quote appropriate and empowering; "...I insist upon my past. I'm entitled to that."[105]   (A quote by Clara Oswald, in *Doctor Who*).

This applies perfectly to my case, and later I learned that I had made the right choice. What I had experienced for the last couple of years was so terrible. The loud and constant noise often made me feel suicidal. Nevertheless, there was no question I wanted to stay and begin this journey with David; after all, there was hope that silence would return, even though the chance was slim.

Learning From The Past

One of the benefits of hypnosis is that it gives you the ability to consciously rediscover forgotten emotions associated with past experiences. To do this, I imagined that I was a time-traveller, going back mentally and emotionally to the past to re-engage with emotions. After all, I, like anyone else, have life experiences that span from my birth to the present moment. The Whispering Exercise on p. 274 is an excellent example of how past emotions can be repaired in the present.

One of the essential things David taught me was to look back without staring because if I stared, I would not be able to see too well since I would be aiming to stare at something specific. It was necessary to identify events and their associated emotions from my past that my conscious thought was unimportant or too painful and, therefore, not worth returning to. I needed to reconnect with those events emotionally and to recognise how I felt at the time without the mask of denial blocking them out. To learn from the emotional part of myself that communicates important emotions from a higher or deeper emotional level, I had to acknowledge that first, it was important to adopt the proper perspective and a settled way of thinking. Then I could change all the other smaller emotions. On my journey of hypnosis, I learned that the weakness is *not* admitting trauma from the past.

The Elephant In The Room

My journey to recovering from tinnitus often took me to dark and unpleasant memories and emotions from my past, mainly related to what it meant to have a disability; I was often tired and depressed. Hypnosis gives a solution to this by providing a way of recognising the whole of us and how we have come to be the people we are today. Through David, I understood depression could be caused when deep, big and powerful issues pass from the subconscious to the conscious and that they must not be prevented from surfacing. In Dream Analysis, the feeling of depression is dark grey. Depression is, in effect, the elephant in the room because elephants are also dark grey. Realising what I already knew about this elephant made it possible to engage with my depression and stop ignoring it, which I had done all my life. As my awareness of the metaphorical elephants in my emotional space enlarged, I witnessed the elephants in the room shrinking to a suitable size where I could observe them properly. They then transformed into problems that I could identify and deal with appropriately. At this point, I realised that depression had been my companion since I was a child; I did not recognise it then because I did not know any different.

Once depression was recognised, I learned to view it as a friend as it reminded me that issues still needed conscious acknowledgement. Depression reminded me that I was on a journey with a definite beginning, middle and end; my approach was not to fight but to welcome and learn from it; this helped my depression to be acknowledged and to pass.

The recovery from tinnitus was like driving through a long tunnel where the tunnel was the same in appearance for its entire length. This sometimes gave the illusion of not moving forward, but in effect, I needed to remind myself that my foot was gently but definitely on the accelerator. Hypnosis ensured that I constantly move forward on my journey through the tunnel to an endpoint which is permanent silence, while I acknowledged my emotional trauma along the way.

I understood that my depression was temporary and necessary. I was persistent in understanding myself better at an emotional level and acknowledging the events that had resulted in such loud and constant noise. After all, everyone has one shot at life, and I took my chances with hypnosis to give me another opportunity to live again, and with David on my side, failure was impossible.

Physiology

There were also effects of acknowledging what the subconscious had revealed, which manifested physically. My energy levels often dropped dramatically, and I felt exhausted when I did nothing. This was because the subconscious was processing emotions with the conscious, which it was still unaccustomed to. This unfamiliar action used up a considerable amount of energy. It was vital for me to rest when needed and to eat when I was hungry rather than at mealtimes. I felt fatigued, affecting my concentration levels and daily interactions with others that only a few understood. I work about ten to twelve hours per day. However, it was sometimes impossible to work at all, or I could only work for a few hours. At first, I felt frustrated and angry about not being productive, but then I realised this was unhelpful. I reminded myself that recovering from tinnitus was the hardest and the most important journey I was on, and while most people were unlikely to recover, I was in the best position to do this. This permitted me to rest and just be.

Unable To Study

Studying for a Ph.D. while undergoing hypnotherapy was quite challenging, but the Ph.D. gave me something else on which to focus. It was a good way of spending my time usefully, which helped me to cope with tinnitus. The work required was to write between 700 and 1500 words daily and read a couple of chapters or research papers. Often the tinnitus made it impossible even to write a sentence, and I would end up in bed for most of the day or stare uncomprehendingly at the television. I marvelled at the fact that I was being allowed to remain on the Ph.D. programme. None of my supervisors' deadlines were met, since it was impossible to predict my productivity on any given day. The unpredictability of tinnitus and how it affected me made concentration impossible.

Nevertheless, my supervisors were understanding and encouraging. I would often take long periods away from my Ph.D., and my principal supervisor would make the appropriate arrangements with the university to make this possible. As I progressed with my applied knowledge of hypnosis, it became possible to reduce the volume of tinnitus quickly, making it viable to do a few hours of work a day.

While treatment towards recovery took time, effort and commitment, I decided that everything, including the multitude of tasks that were once my top priorities, would come second to my daily hypnotherapy practice.

This was the only approach I knew would lead to my complete and lasting recovery from tinnitus. I felt that tinnitus had robbed me of my quality of life and that the knowledge that David had shared gave me the possibility of hearing silence again. It often felt like I was simultaneously studying for two Ph.Ds while people around me thought I was studying for one.

Trusting the Subconscious

Erickson stated, "The things that we know, but don't know we know, give us even more trouble."[106] How can we go from the land of knowing to the land of realising? Only when we engage our emotions to learn what we already know do we begin the journey of recovery. The sound of tinnitus is the end product of unacknowledged emotional trauma, but we need to go back to the roots to understand how trauma came to be and how we feel about it at an emotional level.

As soon as I believed I had consciously understood my past on an emotional level, another unexpected emotion would arise to disrupt the stability of my understanding. Later, I understood that even though, in such circumstances, the process of recovery may not feel stable, this is nothing to be alarmed at because this process needs to occur to gain emotional stability. When all parts of the subconscious have been recognised and understood consciously, they often manifest as characters in dreams (further information about acknowledging inner conflict can be found on p. 164). Sometimes emotions, thoughts and feelings are so unfamiliar and remote from the conscious that I cannot agree with what my subconscious tells me. The best way I dealt with these unexpected, complex and often unwanted emotions and revelations was to accept them as how I truly felt. It was necessary to realise that these emotions were so far removed from my conscious, that I did not recognise them as mine. Therefore, in the recovery from tinnitus, it is vital to arrive at a place where these once-unfamiliar emotional ideas are consciously accepted.

Mutual Cooperation

There should be mutual influence and respect between the conscious and subconscious, because there must be cooperation between the two. The subconscious and the conscious from the whole part of me, where my entire awareness acknowledges both dimensions. Like the leaves of the tree acknowledging the roots, even though both will never inhabit the same space, they are intrinsically connected, and mutually dependent. Such relationships between the subconscious and the conscious are vital. This is because the roots are where the trauma is stored, and the only way to get this trauma out is up through the trunk, through the branches and finally by transpiration through the leaves, where it exits the tree altogether. For this to be possible, all parts of the tree must acknowledge the trauma as it passes through to make sure all the channels are open and not blocked.

Sometimes, what I discovered about my past was extremely painful, so it was vital that I was prepared, open and ready to recognise this. For example, I acknowledged that most people saw me as a young girl who could not understand them when they spoke. This is why some people communicated with me as if I were a toddler when I was a teenager, even when I was a woman. While I knew this subconsciously, my conscious needed to acknowledge this as well.

For instance, I thought I would be a burden to Phil, my best friend, so I consciously decided not to become too close to him and to discourage him from helping me in any way, even though I loved him very much.

He pointed out that I always apologised, even when it was not my fault. For example, one evening, we went out for a meal after swimming and noticing how slowly I ate compared to him, I apologised for this. On reflection, this apologetic behaviour could have stemmed from trying to be accepted in mainstream society, some members of which have been condescending. My subconscious insisted, mostly through Automatic Writing, that I needed a friend whose support and love that I could rely upon. It is common for most people to have favourable perceptions and information about themselves that perpetuates or expands the positivity of their self-concept. This was not the case with me; therefore, my subconscious chose Phil, who is loving and very gentle towards me, which counteracted the suffering that tinnitus gave me. My subconscious understood he had exceptional qualities which were needed for my recovery.

What is worth mentioning here is that I did not know this at a conscious level, but my subconscious insisted that I became close to him and trusted him. I discovered that Phil was easy to love, and he seemed to sense that I needed comfort even though I never told him and extended his friendship warmly. For once, I had someone I wanted to love and who returned the same. As a result, I got what I needed from our friendship and much more than I expected. I discovered that he loved me, which helped me bring up to the surface the love I had for him, which was hidden in the subconscious. He comforted me when I did not know what comfort felt like and was always there when I needed him; he was not like anyone I had known. Phil convinced me to go swimming with him; I did not want to at first because of my experience in my special needs school, where a male teacher had made an inappropriate drawing of me and behaved unprofessionally (see p. 92).

Dan Siegel, a professor of psychiatry at UCLA School of Medicine, writes that,

> "When we attune to others we allow our own internal state to shift, to come to resonate with the inner world of another. This resonance is at the heart of important sense of "feeling felt" that emerges in close relationships."[107]

Trauma, whether subconscious or conscious, takes up emotional energy, unlike love, which gives something back to help trauma be neutralised. It must be the right kind of love, like the key to the door you are attempting to open. The appropriate person with the right kind of love must match the depth and intensity of trauma for it to be neutralised. For me, Phil was this person.

Hypnosis taught me the importance of conscious humility, making it easier to accept and trust the subconscious' wisdom. In return, hypnosis gives me the power not to be a puppet on a string but, instead, the human being I am with the whole spectrum of emotions available to me. Hypnosis gives my conscious a privileged front-row seat to the usually hidden world of the subconscious. I discovered that there is a price for accessing the subconscious as a conscious being, and this is because I do not know what to expect next. Therefore, it is essential to be open to all possibilities and to accept them as they are. The conscious and the subconscious must have a healthy, positive and respectful relationship built on the trust that the conscious will accept whatever the subconscious reveals is true, no matter how painful or traumatic it is for the conscious to assimilate. As I understood this, it became important not to do anything counter to the subconscious' desires, whether I agreed with them at a conscious level or not.

I learned to trust my subconscious enough to know it is always right and that it has my best interests at heart. This trust is crucial even though sometimes I do not agree with the suggestions of the subconscious at a conscious level. It should be noted that the subconscious is not this all-powerful entity that can be trusted implicitly, but, in my case, it has done a far better job than my conscious. Yapko elaborates,

> "The "unconscious" is a global construct that psychologists, psychiatrists, and neuroscientists use to talk about parts of human functioning that take place beyond conscious awareness. It's an abstraction, shorthand. There isn't really a defined entity called "the" unconscious that we can say predictably and reliably does this or that. Instead, we infer principles of its functioning from scientific experimentation and careful observation. From this we learn that the unconscious has some impressive resources and potentials." [108]

Through hypnosis, I learnt the importance of making the conscious decision to trust my subconscious. This was fundamental to my recovery from tinnitus. A shift in my consciousness brought me to the point of feeling love for Phil, my friend. My conscious behaviour and actions towards him changed but only superficially because I recognised the desire of the subconscious. This is how the conscious caught up with the subconscious because conscious actions follow conscious thoughts.

The Perceptions Of Others Contributing To Tinnitus

And like a fog it clung to me

invisibly

penetrating deep within me

without me having a clue what poison it had left

I was burnt from inside with it

but never knew it

as I looked in the mirror

I had disappeared

instead there was a construction of other people's reality

staring back at me

My recovery was a journey to become the person I am today, uncovering my true self. This happened partly through discovering which emotional perceptions of how I saw myself originated from others so that I could discard them.

The conscious does not register or acknowledge subliminal messages, but the subconscious does. This is how negative perceptions from other people can enter the subconscious without being detected consciously. I explore this further in the exercise called Fly-Tipping on p. 301, which helps the subconscious to organise emotions and dispose of other emotions that did not originate from itself. Similarly, but more positively, Phil displayed his affection for me, which taught me that I was a person worthy of love. Here, it is important to note that positive emotions originate from others as well as negative ones. After all, we are all beings affected by interactions with others that we influence.

Merleau-Ponty, a philosopher of phenomenology, highlights,

> "The phenomenological world is not pure being, but the sense which is revealed where the paths of my various experiences intersect, and also where my own and other people's intersect and engage each other like gears."[109]

Life experiences do not happen in a vacuum. It is necessary to recognise emotions and feel conscious of the negative and positive interactions with others if one is to acknowledge their emotional impact on oneself. Even though this is obvious, an effect of tinnitus is the inability to process emotions. I understand how my experiences and interactions with others have shaped me; this was how I could let go of the past and other people's perceptions. I needed Phil's friendship to teach me a new way of perceiving myself; this counteracted all the negative and derogatory perceptions I had of myself, which originated from others throughout my life. This is how I learned to understand the original wisdom of my subconscious.

The Love Of A Friend

We have a fixed idea of how a person should be; they need to stand straight, and to be able to use their hands efficiently and effectively, they have to walk effortlessly too. We do not want or expect to see anything else. If someone is physically unable, we deny those who are different the ability to be themselves. Throughout my upbringing, I had been put down by those I came into contact with. They would make assumptions about my disability and find faults in my personality and behaviour. They aimed to change me to make me a 'better person' while telling me that I needed to improve my social skills to make friends and have better relationships with other people. Some perceived me as less of a woman because of my physical disability, which made no sense. Their impressions left a lasting imprint on the way I saw myself. This perception was stressful, which exacerbated the tinnitus. Phil was easy to love, but I needed my subconscious to tell me. As my friend Phil and I got to know each other, he also could sense my experience and what had gone wrong. Phil provided his perspective on what I had been through, which helped me acknowledge this. This aspect of our friendship was challenging, but I never questioned it since I trusted him. My subconscious reminded me that I needed to acknowledge how Phil saw me and recognise his love for me. Rather than a blob in a wheelchair, through Phil, I learnt I am a woman that can be loved, and that another person can enjoy my company. My subconscious instructed me to do whatever he asked without question. Although this may appear far-fetched, through hypnosis, I learnt that the wisdom of my subconscious is far superior to my conscious. My subconscious realised that Phil's approach to me was what was necessary for me to recover from tinnitus. This provided me with a new way of viewing myself, which was more in line with who I was emotionally and in line with my subconscious. This is just one way Phil became crucial to my recovery.

Phil reflected on what I lacked emotionally and helped me feel like other women do. He recognised that I was locked into my disability, something I felt but could never bring to conscious awareness and articulate into words. His love for me stripped away my emotional straightjacket that I did not realise I had on because I always wore it. It felt restrictive, but it was the only normality that I knew. Phil is the first friend who has been there, regardless of the circumstances and has encouraged me to realise that I am just a woman who needs and deserves love.

Sophia and Sapna

And tomorrow's child am I

for this library with the wisdom of tomorrow contained within them

break out of hell

the knowledge book says

break out of hell under that spell

in that well

break out of isolation

break out of captivity and be free

captivate your audience with your smile

let them hear your laughter all the while

but it is all very well me talking like this but I was a child in a special

needs hell

and the butterfly sat on my shoulder one day

he told me a story about a girl a long time ago that he knew

and then he narrated my history and my destiny all at the same time

it was a story that wouldn't be mine because I didn't recognise it

it didn't belong to me

or so I thought

it belonged to some other person I didn't know look in the mirror, and

who do you see?

The woman standing before me turned into grains of sand in front of my

eyes and if I could walk through the mirror I could touch her

touch the grains of sand

she is dead now

she is turning into dust and must go now

I blew away the dust from my fingers and toes where I stood

I blew away life itself

too much of a history we had together

the girl and I who used to stand in the mirror staring at me

I could see the pain in her eyes

back then of course the pain was connected to me by some invisible

thread of destiny

I could not feel the pain inside myself

it was surrounded by numbness under a hard shell

I decided to help this girl in the mirror one more time

I asked her a question and she gave me a reply

I asked her who were you before you were born?

I am Sophia

came the reply

I'm you of course but you didn't know

I'm you with far to go

I'm all that is you and will ever be you

but I'm not a girl

I'm a woman of course

just like you

so don't blow me away on a sunny day

I have a right to be heard

so listen to me

I have a right to you know what

but you deny my femininity one more time

you deny my right to be free the conscious part of me

I am the emotions trapped

they are trapped inside of me

but they are your emotions

of course waiting to be free

now go away the conscious part of me and break out of hell

break this mirror

for you are well

I'm you

and if you smash this I will come through

break it now Sapna

I order you to

thank you very much

Sapna

for breaking the mirror of hell

I'm here now for I'm well

join me Sophia I say

join me now it's a new day

join up the writing on the wall

join up with us

and we can stand tall

join up with us

and we can fly through the rainbow skies

join up with us

and we can enter a new day

why don't you do that

Sophia?

And come to me

for I'm your sister

I am your destiny and so subconsciously

I joined up with her again

and that is the end

My subconscious has since expressed the backstory of how I came to have tinnitus, though metaphorical, is entirely accurate. This story was played out over time and came to my conscious awareness through the narrative of my dreams and Automatic Writing.

My name is Sapna, and my subconscious has used this name to distinguish the conscious from itself. My feminine subconscious has told my conscious that its name is Sophia, wisdom, and this is how my conscious acknowledges the original true wisdom of my subconscious. One day some years ago, this sentence came out through Automatic Writing:

I am Sophia

Sophia is my name

I am Sophia

Wisdom is my game

The way silence returned is that my subconscious, which mostly expressed itself as Sophia (my original emotional wisdom), made itself known to Sapna (my conscious self). Through the work of the subconscious through hypnosis, Sophia (my subconscious self) remembered her original wisdom, inaccessible to her because of the trauma I consciously experienced as Sapna. The paradox of Sophia forgetting her wisdom was the root cause of my tinnitus. My emotional trauma had suppressed this wisdom into the subconscious and made it inaccessible to my conscious.

Young children are their natural selves, but as society and their immediate interactions with other people become dominant, the way they perceive themselves becomes diluted or changed by the perceptions of others. This is typical, but it was carried to excess and, in my case, this was imposed on me due to the interpretations of my disability. For example, Sophia, my female subconscious part, could not remember her wisdom because of my childhood experience. This paradox gave rise to my emotional disconnection, causing tinnitus later in life.

Jack

Although Sophia is my subconscious' prominent female voice, other smaller voices have originated from a lifetime of interaction. Jack is a strong male voice who first presented himself as being in love with Sophia and being her partner. More crucially, he was not blinded by my trauma, allowing him to perceive all that was wrong in my life. Sophia's paradox of losing her wisdom was remedied by Jack by reminding her of all that she had forgotten.

However, Jack was wrongly imprisoned by how I perceived myself as a woman and even though he could still communicate, he needed Sophia to recognise his imprisonment to free him. Jack understands my emotional trauma, articulates what happened, and reflects on it while providing suggestions and advice. Jack is still there, but he decided to become dormant after another has embodied him in the physical world, which was his wish. Jack's aim for me was to re-engage with love and to experience the whole emotion of love in the external world, which is how I finally recovered from tinnitus.

The Black Widow Spider

From David, I learnt that my subconscious and conscious had to re-establish their connection to smooth communication between the two. This would mean that the conscious could immediately feel an emotion that originated in the subconscious because of external stimuli.

I watched a nature programme one day, and it was about the Black Widow spider. I learned spider silk was strong and produced at will by the spider: there is no limit to the quantity that could be made. This was my inspiration for the way I would re-establish the connection between the conscious and the subconscious. It was limitless, durable, and lasting, like spider silk.

The Black Widow spider eats her mate after mating. Instead of this, Jack, the male part of me, became more integrated into Sophia, which gave her easy access to his wisdom. I am an animal lover and avoid causing them harm, but it is for this reason that I am cautious not to harm spiders.

My Care-taker

I imagine my subconscious to be the caretaker of my conscious, whereas the conscious is superficial and childlike and needs a responsible adult to take care of it and guide it. This is the subconscious' domain. That does not mean that my subconscious dominates my conscious, but it has a responsibility towards the conscious; in return, it can express itself. The conscious must be open and willing to be led by the subconscious. If this is not the case, it will create a barrier between the subconscious and itself, making the tinnitus louder. This is the fundamental principle that I had to realise at a conscious and a subconscious level during my journey to recovery.

The Subconscious And Its Relationship To The Conscious

The aim of recovery is for the conscious and the subconscious to have the same emotional perspective and knowledge about memories and experiences with their associated emotions. To do this, messages from the subconscious must pass into the conscious, so it learns from the subconscious. David told me that some never complete the recovery process because this journey is arduous and painful. In my case, the acknowledgement was far less traumatic than being forced to listen to tinnitus and being powerless to stop it. This encouraged me to use hypnosis to defy the conventional 'wisdom' of medical professionals who deemed tinnitus incurable.

In the dying embers of a fire that lasted out
I was lost in between the branches of the trees
for life had unfolded the wrong way
what I saw was another girl's reality
I'd entered another timeline again
and in a parallel world somewhere else I was missing
I was where I shouldn't have been
reality was interrupted and made to wait
for destiny was waiting for me but no one saw that
did they?
My future hung in the balance
the wormhole that I'd entered had closed up there was no going back to
my reality
something happened one day
that changed the future of me
I'd bumped into hypnosis
which had transported me back to where I was meant to be on the path
I was meant to be before life had made a mistake

I was ticked off wrongly on the register of time
I could not walk a mile in another person's shoes for they hurt too much
and I was bruised
so I stopped walking and stood still
until I'd found a slip stream somewhere in my mind's eye and entered
my reality through the back door
and I was home again
ready to carry on in the future
that was meant for me

Trusting Hope

There were occasions when my tinnitus was extremely loud after starting hypnotherapy. These times were difficult mentally and even physically because of the way tinnitus affected my physical disability. Through David, I had learnt that it was unwise to become stressed since this would worsen the tinnitus; counter-intuitively, a mindset of radical acceptance that encouraged a deeper sense of calmness and relaxation was beneficial. David taught me a useful saying: "Don't push the river; it flows by itself". This served as a reminder that sometimes the subconscious needed the time and space to be left alone. Over time, I learnt when it was beneficial to intervene with hypnosis and when to just be.

When I experienced loud tinnitus, a helpful 'mantra' that I thought of was: "I am experiencing loud tinnitus right now, but I am not this tinnitus... I am far more than this". Yapko describes selective attention as "...the ability to voluntarily focus on one portion of an experience while tuning out the rest."[110] This helped me to get through the day and to cope with the ever-so-loud noise that I was experiencing. When a person is aware of focusing on something, this automatically removes their attention from another stimulus which, in my case, was tinnitus. I reminded myself that silence had occurred previously and would happen again. The bases for my optimism was that I was learning hypnotherapy exercises and methods and expanding my understanding of the relationship between the subconscious and the conscious. This kept me sane while providing me with confidence that tomorrow would be a better day and that I knew what to do in the present. I needed the time and space to think clearly about everything I had learnt, which was often easier thought of than done because of the sound I was experiencing. If I was stuck for ideas, I would ask my subconscious to provide a solution or insight as to why my tinnitus was so loud, which it often would eloquently do through Automatic Writing (see p. 122).

Chapter 9

Automatic Writing And

My Subconscious

Over time, I have learned how to initiate the subconscious to express itself through the written word. This chapter explains the method of Automatic Writing and then describes practical exercises, moving on to the concept of Clean Language and its use. Finally, it examines the Focusing method, where the subconscious is able to explore an issue and find a resolution.

Automatic Writing

And now round the roundabout we go hoping for a miracle of some sort
but nothing comes my way except words on a page unrecognisable to
me they form sentences
stanzas
poetry
words march out in an orderly fashion from my subconscious mind
giving me a narrative of my history in poetry format
they arrange themselves by themselves on the page

life's lesson is spelled out before me

wisdom rises like smoke from my subconscious mind

reminding me of the pain that I once had forgotten

it inhabits the page now and not me

lightening up my load subconsciously

until there's nothing left of the pain now except poetry

I just have pages of pain now

not in me though

as I share them with other people

I watch my waters flow

if words had weight there would be tons of the stuff

an exquisite subconscious expression of pain

mostly second hand though given to me by others

when I was too young to understand how to separate glass

plastics and paper

and how to throw away second hand stuff from my house

so I don't want your rubbish any more

I say

and I have done enough recycling until today now I fill myself up with

silence and love

My Discovery Of Automatic Writing`　　　`

I happened to chance upon a book about Automatic Writing by a well-known psychiatrist and author Anita Mary Mühl, who was a practising psychologist in the early part of the nineteenth century. Unlike so many others, this book was not about the supernatural but Automatic Writing as a form of psychological treatment and practice. This book sparked my curiosity to learn more about this writing method; it became the basis for my Automatic Writing practice. Later on, I discovered that Pierre Janet, a practising psychologist from the late 1800s to the mid-1900s, was the first to recognise that a person's experience of their past affects their current emotional state. He was also the first to propose that the conscious, which is responsible for critical thought, lay over the subconscious, which had a powerful awareness. Janet, an early proponent of Automatic Writing for accessing the subconscious, was disappointed about the way this was hijacked by pseudo-science. Janet studied this psychological phenomenon as "...a cathartic treatment" where, under hypnosis, a patient could write, if asked, things which they could not consciously remember."[111] Automatic Writing was described by Anita Mühl as "...script which the writer produces *involuntarily* and in some instances without being aware of the process, although he may be (and generally is) in an alert waking state."[112] This is an accurate description of my experience with Automatic Writing.

Somnambulism is a condition where part of a person's personality dissociates from the rest, preventing them from consciously accessing memories and past emotions. In my case, this led to tinnitus, as outlined in the introduction. Automatic Writing allows the subconscious to express itself without the conscious influencing it. Irene Tobis Ph.D., an American psychologist with over thirty years of experience in several settings with an interest in physical and psychological health and John F. Kihlstrom, is a cognitive social psychologist whose passion is in cognition in personal and social contexts and social interactions. They propose that automatic processing does not take up resources because it is automatised since it is possible for the subconscious to carry out parallel processing effortlessly. Automatic processing does not intervene with other processes because they do not consume attentional resources.[113] The conscious can take a back seat in Automatic Writing.

A Brief History Of Automatic Writing

I discovered that the method of Automatic Writing is unfortunately also associated with the supernatural, which may be why it is not used in clinical psychological practice. Unfortunately, it is hijacked by pseudo-science and, in particular, supernaturalists and mediums who worked in the Victorian Era when belief in the supernatural was prevalent. The so-called mediums would either use Ouija boards or write automatically, claiming that spirits had entered them when expressing themselves through Automatic Writing. In reality, this practice was the subconscious coming through to write automatically and had no connection to the supernatural or communicating with the dead. Even so, scientists have distanced themselves greatly from Automatic Writing because of its association with the occult; it is a shame that such a powerful psychological tool was disregarded as pseudo-science.

However, Boris Sidis, a Ukrainian-American psychologist, physician, psychiatrist, and philosopher of education in the 1900s, was curious about hypnotic states. He was also interested in Automatic Writing from a scientific and psychological perspective; thus, he took an experimental approach to mental processes. Sidis put people in two categories, those who were completely unaware of their act of writing and those who knew about what they were doing but did not associate their writing with themselves. Sidis outlined the conditions for Automatic Writing; he said,

> "To induce the first stages of automatic writing the same conditions are requisite as those of normal suggestibility. The subject starting his first lesson in automatic writing must strongly *concentrate* his attention on some letter, figure, or word; he must *distract* his attention from what is going on in his

hand; he must be in a *monotonous* environment; he must not be disturbed by a variety of incoming sense impressions; he must keep quiet, thus *limiting his voluntary movements; his field of consciousness must be contracted;* no other ideas but the requisite ones should be present in the mind; and if other ideas and images do enter his mind, they must be *inhibited*."[114]

Even though Automatic Writing was developed in the nineteenth century, it perfectly captures all I experience when I practise it.

The *Scientific American* magazine from 1886 describes the planchette for Automatic Writing as,

"A heart-shaped piece of board, mounted upon three supports. It is seven inches from the depression in the base of the heart to its apex, and seven inches measured across its widest part. Two of the supports are legs of wood or brass, terminating in pentagram wheels or casters, usually of iron, bone, or hard rubber. The third support is a pencil thrust through a socket at the apex of the heart."[115]

This encouraged an experimental and open-minded approach to Automatic Writing, which may have discouraged pseudo-science from hijacking this practice. Due to this method, sceptics needed to wait for more conclusive evidence while explaining that the boundary between the conscious and the subconscious may not be clear-cut. It was thought that the right hemisphere of the brain could be responsible for the way Automatic Writing is produced. Later, on p. 175, I make a similar assumption.

Myers recognised early on that Automatic Writing was a way for the subconscious to express itself. He said,

> "In our ignorance, we simply know that certain complex facts, like an intelligent reply to a question, depend upon two things which we believe associated; superior cerebral mechanism and a phenomenon which we call an effect of consciousness. We find the same characteristics in the so-called subconscious phenomena, and we must suppose back to them the same two conditions."[116]

Automatic Writing was finally breaking away from the notion that it was only associated with the supernatural. Finally, it had the potential to have real recognition in the scientific community. Alfred Binet, a French psychologist, described an experiment that he undertook in 1889; he said,

> "We put a pen into the anaesthetic hand, and we make it write a word; left to itself the hand preserves its attitude, and at the expiration of a short space of time repeats the word, often five or ten times. Having arrived at this fact, we again seize the anaesthetic hand, and cause it to write some familiar word, for example, the patient's own name; but in so doing, we intentionally commit an error in spelling. In its turn the anaesthetic hand

repeats the word, but oddly enough, the hand betrays a momentary hesitation when it reaches the letter at which the error in orthography was committed; if a superfluous letter happens to have been added, sometimes the hand will hesitatingly re-write the name along with the supplementary letter; again it will retrace only a part of the letter in question; and again, finally, entirely suppress it."
117

This may have been the first indication that Automatic Writing was not under the conscious control of the writer. Binet, like Janet, assumed that the writing must have come from the subconscious since the correction of the spelling mistake could only have occured by a process of thought. Some similar experiments by Binet later proved the same. In one experiment, Binet placed a piece of paper with writing at such a distance that was too far for the subject to read. He asked the subject to write what she thought was written, which she did accurately. This demonstrated that a greater visual acuity of the second consciousness could be revealed, said Binet, through Automatic Writing. Binet concluded that the subconscious picked up the message, even though it was too far away for the conscious to register. [118]

Binet concluded that this was evidence of double consciousness (conscious and subconscious) which he first discovered in "hysterical" patients but which was also prevalent in "normal" subjects. He concluded that Automatic Writing is one proof of this, among many others.

My First Experiences Of Automatic Writing

After reading Anita Mühl's book *Automatic Writing*, I tried writing automatically, and my tinnitus dramatically reduced with immediacy; it was another exciting discovery. This was the first time I had eczema, and I thought there might be a correlation between eczema and Automatic Writing. I wanted to ensure this was not by chance, but the same happened the next day when I wrote automatically. After investigation, I discovered that the eczema resulted from emotional stress, which was a positive sign since it strongly suggested that the Automatic Writing had brought up painful and difficult emotional memories, which was crucial to recovering from tinnitus. Even though the eczema was bad initially, I found that the tinnitus would either reduce or disappear for the day. Since eczema was far easier to deal with than tinnitus, I found myself motivated to continue Automatic Writing while developing this technique.

Through the daily practice of Automatic Writing, the conscious witnesses and learns the articulation of the subconscious without influencing it. This has proved a vital part of my daily practice in allowing memories, thoughts, feelings and emotions that were once out of bounds to my conscious self to surface consciously. The first few times after undertaking an Automatic Writing session, I often felt mentally exhausted and felt the need to sleep or at least rest. This was because powerful emotions from the subconscious were surfacing and being acknowledged. Gradually this became less tiring, and I can now continue daily life while being able to write automatically.

The Ideal Time To Write Automatically

At first, I practised writing automatically at the same time each day so that my subconscious became accustomed to revealing itself daily. The environment in which I wrote was usually quiet, which is essential during this process. I ensured that I was not interrupted, so my phone was silent, and I sometimes asked others not to disturb me for the next hour. This reduced potential distractions, so the conscious and the subconscious know not to be concerned and that this time was dedicated to the subconscious expressing itself.

Eventually, I could practise Automatic Writing whenever it suited my schedule, which worked well. However, I discovered that Automatic Writing works best at the end of the day. The subconscious, at this time, informs the conscious about what it fails to fully or partly acknowledge in daily life. This also prevents emotions from being carried over to the next day, making dreams less vivid, and improving sleep. When you first practise Automatic Writing, you may prefer to write in the morning since it is likely to reduce tinnitus, providing relief for the rest of the day.

Since I am a private person, one day, I felt unsure about whether I should reveal so much of my life in this book. The following Automatic Writing is where the subconscious reflects on this, giving me a definite answer. I have added punctuation in the Automatic Writing below to make it easier to read.

> *I think your book is great. Moving on a little bit, I want you to be careful of one thing, Sophia, that you are consciously comfortable with it all. And I know you're confused at the moment, but the way I see it, is that the trauma doesn't belong to you*

anymore but the memories do, and for once, Sophia, open up yourself to the world and let other people feel your pain. And what you have gone through, and maybe they will feel embarrassed about the world they live in and serves them right too. So, if I were your conscious mind, I'd do it. Please end this automatic writing now.

We experience many events during the day that has an emotional impact on us, big or small. As I became used to acknowledging how I emotionally felt from moment to moment, it was possible to keep the tinnitus at bay. I still undertake Automatic Writing before sleep. Sometimes my subconscious has a lot to say, while at other times, it does not. I found that doing Automatic Writing at this time of the day allows my conscious to catch up with the subconscious and for the subconscious to inform and advise the conscious about its perspective on the day's events and to provide suggestions on solving dilemmas and problems. Since the subconscious is constantly witnessing all that I experience, this is ideal for it to provide an informed opinion from an emotional perspective, which is something I may not have fully acknowledged consciously.

This method of daily communication, as well as dreaming, prevents the build-up of emotions in the subconscious, which, as we know, if left unchecked, could lead to the tinnitus returning. I see my subconscious as a friend who keeps me safe daily and has my best interests at heart. This is because the subconscious is not motivated by the ego or the need to fulfil unrealistic wishes that are not good for me, nor is it motivated by selfishness, which is why it is "pure". I encourage readers to undertake daily Automatic Writing, if possible.

Grief, Loss, and Automatic Writing

During the final stages of writing this book, I was bereaved since my mother passed away. Emotionally, I was in a pit somewhere inside myself, unable to climb out; grief had put me there with no means of escape. When you are experiencing your own grief and loss, and if you have tinnitus, emotions may not be surfacing consciously, which may lead to the tinnitus becoming louder or, in my case, returning. I hardly talked to my family and cut myself off from my friends since I could no longer bear human company. On the day of the funeral, I stayed in bed and sobbed; I have always been a quiet person, never sharing my feelings with anyone. I was desperate for Phil's company; his special way of comforting me had always made life bearable, but I could not see him because of the pandemic.

As always, I wrote automatically every night before I slept; the process during those days made me sob. Even though Automatic Writing was torture at that time, I knew I needed to pursue it since the blocked emotions would give rise to tinnitus again.

I thought correctly; Automatic Writing proved to be a way that the subconscious relieved itself of the strong and overwhelming emotions that would have remained there otherwise, as dreaming was insufficient. Through Automatic Writing, my subconscious reminded me that it was there for me, simultaneously providing comfort. It also advised me on making plans without my mother and how to cope practically and emotionally. Automatic Writing is a powerful tool that helped me survive a major and life-changing loss by providing the subconscious with the means to express itself to the conscious. Through Automatic Writing, we have the resources to cope with all we encounter.

Ideal Conditions For Automatic Writing

I am unable to use my hands to write, so before I had a specialised computer (explained later), I dictated what I wanted to write to my Personal Assistant. The words appeared on the monitor, and I checked if she had typed correctly. The computer screen was blank, the writing window was made smaller, so a few words were visible at a time so that the conscious did not complete the thoughts expressed by the subconscious by deriving meaning from the words already typed. Doing so helps to avoid distractions. No matter how small, distractions can influence the writing, which must be avoided at all costs since the subconscious can easily create a barrier. For those who can use their hands, I recommend you use a more conventional method of writing with paper and pen. During this process, ensure that the paper is hidden from your view and that the pen is in contact with the paper at all times. The pen and paper may not be in contact when you are concentrating on writing automatically.

On my first attempt, I was not sure what, if anything, would come out, but something did emerge. Having never written poetry before, I was surprised when the Automatic Writing came out in rhyme. Since then, the writing has become stronger and deeper in content. I often read back a piece of writing that I do not understand; the overriding aspect of this work is to allow the subconscious to express itself in any way it wishes. An advantage of Automatic Writing can be to release pent-up emotions by expressing internal emotional conflicts and bringing up forgotten memories and their emotional associations. I often use the method of Roads and Roundabouts (which I will explain in the next chapter) without necessarily writing down anything to ask the subconscious to advise on what I need to do when I am unsure at a conscious level. The advice and insight from the subconscious is like having an extremely close friend who is always available and has my best interests at heart, and knows me better than I know myself at a conscious level.

According to what I have read, not everyone is able to undertake Automatic Writing, though some people can, after practice, while others can perform this straight away. Fortunately, I fall into the latter category, hugely benefiting my mental health.

Often, I do not recognise the writing in front of me since it feels like it has been written by another person. This was why Automatic Writing was so appealing to mediums and supernaturalists, even though the method is anything but supernatural. Gilligan suggests that trance is, "...natural and integral to consciousness, not artificial. In this naturalistic view, trance occurs whenever identity is destabilised, as a means by which identity can be deconstructed and reconstructed." [119]

Self-Identity

When the conscious identity is broken down, the conscious walks on unstable ground. The conscious is used to familiarity and comfort; it wants to know where it is regularly going. Above all, it wants to remain safe, even if it does not acknowledge the reality of emotional pain. In a book called *Pain, The Science Of Suffering* by Patrick Wall, the following sentence is a good summary of this, "Within himself, he displayed the complete syndrome of the best tactics for recovery in people or animals: don't move, and don't let anyone else move you, just sleep."[120] In reference to this, Wall narrated the story of a Swiss army officer who went skiing with his squad. The officer had a skiing accident, severely injuring himself with pain all over his body. Even though my pain did not originate from a physical injury, what struck me was the description of the officer's physical pain which was an accurate account of the way tinnitus affected me and how my conscious did not want me to "move" emotionally. The tinnitus resonated all over me, which is why it felt emotionally paralysing. I wanted to shut everyone out at an emotional level for fear of them "moving" me and causing greater pain.

If the conscious self were asked to break down its identity, this would destabilise it. This is because identity is like a solid bridge that the conscious self can walk upon because it knows it is solid and reliable. As a disabled woman, I cannot help but wonder how I can be fully observed when those observing are biased. It is not justified for them to judge what I should be like when they may not be so critical of themselves, and people tend to be less critical of able-bodied people. The judgements and opinions took away my right and ability to build my self-identity at a conscious level. A study indicates that "...self-defining memories and future thoughts are organized in networks that play important roles in sustaining personal identity..."[121] This is why young people, whether they have a disability or not, should be treated with respect so that their identity maps in the conscious are good and positive, closely matching those in the subconscious. With hypnosis, one can alter habitual behaviour, allowing one part of the brain to take charge when another part usually does this. Society was reluctant to accept me, firstly as a child and then as a woman with thoughts, feelings, emotions and intellect. It was as if they tried to mould me into the person they expected I should be, but if I were able-bodied, perhaps people would not treat me as such an easy target.

Acknowledging Inner Conflict

Sometimes in Automatic Writing, a dialogue between two or more characters may emerge. These characters are extensions of our personalities, like in Dream Analysis. By allowing these characters freedom to express themselves, it is possible to understand the conflict within the subconscious, which provides insight to the origins of my trauma. This is why the exploration of my inner conflict proved to be invaluable in my recovery. Sometimes the characters that emerge are unpleasant and violent in the way they express themselves. While this may be stressful in the moment, it is vital for these parts of me to be heard and acknowledged.

At other times, characters that are loving and caring towards me may also express their views. In my experience, if parts of me are left unheard and not acknowledged, this will manifest as tinnitus. When unpleasant characters emerge in my writing, I am not frightened by this process since they are the formations of past emotional experiences that have not been processed or consciously acknowledged. Even though this is often emotionally traumatic, I am aware that the different characters cannot harm me in any way. Instead, they are desperate to be recognised by my conscious. These characters and the pleasant ones can be viewed as teachers with emotional knowledge of my history. The emotional aspects of my past need to be explored with curiosity, compassion and appropriate fierceness. When working with difficult aspects of our psyche, the late New Zealander psychologist David Grove stressed the importance of "getting them to confess their strengths", which is why I listen to them respectfully.

The example below is the Automatic Writing that I did when I first began using this technique which is why punctuation is used. Later, I found that punctuation hindered Automatic Writing because it engaged with the conscious. The subsequent Automatic Writing without punctuation proved to be more fluid and came out easier.

This Automatic Writing is from the strong, male and loving part of me, who later introduced himself as Jack. Below he reflects on his relationship with me and how and why he came to be, demonstrating how the subconscious can reflect not only on conscious thoughts but also on itself and its relationship to me. He also contemplates the external world while simultaneously coherently explaining my conscious relationship to this male part of me in the subconscious, one which the conscious will understand. I wrote the Automatic Writing below before discovering the benefit of not using punctuation.

04.04.2013

I'm your teacher, I'm your educator, you are my maker and you created me from within because everyone put you in the bin, but you are not dim from within which is why you created me, you see. I'm the man inside, not wanting to hide and giving back your dignity, you see and your right to be free to live with me. But not in fear for you are so near and you are such a dear to me and I'm always here for you to see me inside you guiding you through and through because I know what to do for you and about you because I'm you, Sophia, through and through. But I'm the male part of you Sophia and never forget that OK for I will be in dismay. These words before you that you see on this page are not from you, OK but from me, so don't be in dismay. I'm separate from you but I'm a part of you like conjoined twins, with separate identities but together we rest at ease.

All my love, Jack, back again tomorrow, Sophia, so don't worry about that because I'm Jack and I'm back.

Jack points out that the words are not from me, but have been produced by him. This is evidence that the subconscious has the ability to not only reflect on my emotions but also on its relationship with me as a conscious being.

Over time these characters express themselves, providing their perspectives on why and how I came to be the way I am while highlighting problems and issues I have encountered. They use metaphors to explain their backstories which are the same as metaphors in Dream Analysis (see p. 230). It is as if a silent and invisible part of me that has witnessed all that I have experienced throughout my life has been given a means of expression through Automatic Writing. This is why it is crucial that the conscious allows Automatic Writing to happen via the Roads and Roundabouts Exercise and that this is initiated by the conscious.

Part C - Subconscious Expression

"As my sufferings mounted I soon realized that there were two ways in which I could respond to my situation - either to react with bitterness or seek to transform the suffering into a creative force. I decided to follow the latter course." - Martin Luther King Jr.[122]

Jack demonstrates that my subconscious can and does express itself to the conscious, meaning that the subconscious can talk back to you if you let it. Gilligan suggests that when faced with a problem, we tend to shut down out of fear or anger, attempting to force a change.[123] This tension keeps us stuck and unable to move to a resolution. The way out of this predicament is to accept the situation as it is, without wishful thinking or wishing the situation away. If we want to change something, firstly, it becomes necessary to accept it for what it is; Gilligan describes this as creative acceptance. This does not mean we need to passively submit to whatever we experience. However, Gilligan suggests to "...develop a deep and curious connection with something in a way that opens it to further possibilities."[124]

My disability is severe, and I hate it; why would I think otherwise? It is impossible to get rid of my Cerebral Palsy because there is no cure for it; this is why I need to acknowledge my disability for what it is to accept it and recognise how I feel towards it. Gilligan suggests that the subconscious has infinite possibilities, allowing us to create new realities.[125] When we lose the ability to consider multiple possible meanings, this narrows our field of vision and the way we see the world. For example, my disability brought me closer to hypnosis and to my friend Phil. Here I name two positive experiences that have given me huge pleasure and the ability for growth even though I immensely hate having Cerebral Palsy.

Gilligan explains that accepting and working with what causes us emotional distress is possible.

> "The principle of creative acceptance begins with joining something as it is, not trying to change it. This is not merely an intellectual trick; complete acceptance means opening a generative field to receive it, absorbing it into your somatic center, and finding the cognitive associations (names, beliefs, associational networks) distinguishing it."[126]

For my entire life, I have been told what to do, how to behave, what to say, and even what to wear on many occasions. Some able-bodied people believe that since I am physically disabled, they have the right to shape my life and even myself according to what they deem suitable for me. As Gilligan suggests, hypnosis enabled me to uncover and discard my imposed identity. It was then possible to rediscover who I really am and embody this at a conscious level. Through hypnosis, I learnt that I was not the disabled woman who felt nothing at all but that I had a voice that could answer back; this is how I learnt to stand my ground.

Chapter 10

Automatic Writing

Automatic Writing enables the subconscious to express itself without conscious intrusion, and this technique has numerous benefits. This method, however, will vary from person to person and should be implemented with care and at one's discretion. Although Automatic Writing does not interfere with mental processes or cause suffering, this method of writing is not under the conscious control of the writer's intentions, plans or strategies. Furthermore, it is not necessarily the case that conscious awareness is the result of Automatic Writing. While researching for this chapter, most of what I found was about the supernatural, while the rest of the research was from the early part of the nineteenth century. I could not find relevant information from the current times, which suggests that Automatic Writing is not a modern practice. Despite this, it has empowered me to take control of my mental health and has contributed to my understanding of what my subconscious needs to reveal to the conscious.

Primitive Consciousness

The primitive consciousness creates unlimited versions of itself.

According to Stephen Gilligan, "...primitive consciousness by itself is not especially generative; its evolutionary (or generative change) rate is slow. It creates endless versions of itself, only very slowly growing beyond itself."[127] Gilligan promotes the idea that the primitive consciousness lacks self-awareness and systemic wholeness, where identity is constructed at the ego level. This could mean that these multiple versions of primitive consciousness are the barriers between the conscious and the subconscious, preventing the subconscious from entering conscious awareness. This could be one way the conscious can block out traumatic memories and emotions stored in the subconscious. Since we have no way of knowing about the attempts made by the subconscious to communicate, we also need to be aware that the conscious needs assistance in breaking down this barrier. Being aware of the existence of such a barrier could be the first step to initiating its breakdown to develop the ability for the subconscious to effectively come into the conscious.

Through my experience of recovery, I learnt that the subconscious is aware which is entering the territory of the conscious because it reflects upon information that is usually only in the conscious; my subconscious expresses traumatic experiences through dreams and Automatic Writing, which provides me with a deeper emotional perspective to what I have consciously experienced. Usually, the conscious is unaware of its limitations and that it is a barrier to the subconscious expressing itself. Therefore, it became imperative that I was aware of this at a conscious level, so my conscious could start to weaken this barrier to limit the conflict between the subconscious and the conscious. At this point, the conscious should not prevent the subconscious from entering its domain but rather cooperate to facilitate its expression.

Foundation Exercise - Roads And Roundabouts

I had written automatically previously just by accident. Upon reading Mühl's book, I had better success in Automatic Writing but with some conscious interference. I thought it would be amazing to channel all that noise into words that my subconscious could express whenever it wanted; as I listened to my tinnitus, I thought about this issue for a while. I needed a metaphor to remind the subconscious that tinnitus was not the only way it had to express itself. By definition, this created more than a single option. This led me to consider the kind of metaphor that had multiple options, which the subconscious could use to channel emotions to express themselves in words, not noise. It was an interesting and unusual problem, not something someone would think about after eating their evening meal, but I did one night. The Automatic Writing I had done so far made me consider how to refine this technique. I thought that the metaphor of a roundabout, with its multiple options, provides the subconscious with the ability to choose its direction.

I was amazed when I tried the Roads and Roundabouts exercise since the Automatic Writing came out immediately, and the tinnitus went down. Thinking this was by chance, I performed this exercise again and had the same result. I felt excited about this discovery but could not share it with anyone except David. I was aware of how insignificant it was to other people but how imperative it was to me. That night, I made some notes about this little experiment. My nephew came over the following weekend, and as we were having fun in the garden, I asked him to try it, too, as I described this exercise to him. He was astonished to come up with a rhyme appropriate for his young age, which could indicate that the Roads and Roundabouts exercise, which I will outline later, could be done by others as well.

When I first practised Automatic Writing, I found that the conscious would have something to say in the writing. This was less than ideal in treating tinnitus since it did not reduce tinnitus by much. Then I came up with the Roads and Roundabouts exercise, preventing conscious expression from influencing the writing. It is like wanting to hear the thoughts of one twin only to find that their sibling talks as well. Distracting the conscious twin allows the subconscious twin to speak without interruption. Automatic Writing is best undertaken when the conscious is distracted since this is the domain of the subconscious. The process of Automatic Writing stops as soon as my conscious engages with this process; this is why the Roads and Roundabouts exercise is so effective.

Even though this exercise is mechanical or habit-like, particularly suitable for the conscious way of working, the different roundabout exits may remind the subconscious that there are multiple directions and options to take. Tinnitus is like the driver of a car driving into a dead end. This is why a roundabout was a suitable metaphor since it was a reminder that the subconscious could take several directions (options). It also reminded the subconscious that it had the ability to choose where it wanted to go; it now takes over. I imagine this is how the subconscious breaks through the barrier of the conscious. Through this, the tinnitus is channelled into expressing itself through Automatic Writing, which is ideal since, tinnitus results from unexpressed emotions within the subconscious, as I have outlined in the Introduction.

The Roads And Roundabouts Exercise - Automatic Writing

I imagine I am in a car driving along a quiet and empty road. There are green fields on either side, and I see the road ahead on a beautiful, sunny, calm day, and there are no distractions. As I look into the distance, I see the first roundabout with three exits going in different directions. I see the roundabout coming nearer and nearer, and as I approach it, I take two cycles of inhalation and exhalation.

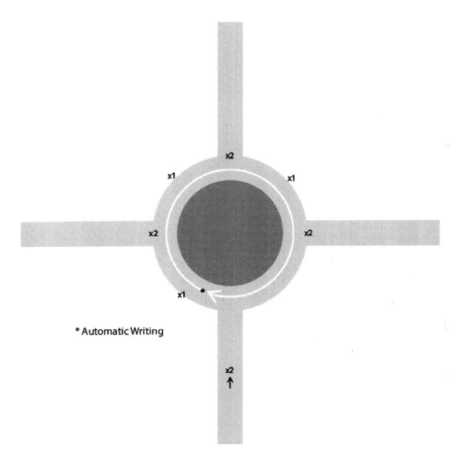

* Automatic Writing

When I enter the roundabout, I acknowledge the space between where I entered and the approaching exit with two inhales and two exhales, accompanied by thinking about the number 1 with every inhale. This number is arbitrary and could efficiently work with any other number or letter of the alphabet. I also acknowledge the exit itself by thinking about the number 1 while taking two cycles of inhaling and exhaling. The point of this is to add another layer of conscious engagement; the conscious is fully occupied at multiple levels, preventing it from distracting the subconscious. During this process, if you find words or some thoughts enter the conscious, think about the number one thousand or another arbitrary number or word with two syllables. Adding an extra syllable may provide a better seal to prevent the conscious from expressing itself.

I repeat this cycle of breaths and engage the conscious with every exit and the space between them until I return to just before where I entered the roundabout. I go past my original entrance without going past the first exit and remain somewhere between the two. Words come into my mind from the subconscious; this is Automatic Writing.

I stop imagining this scene to write these words. Once the Automatic Writing has stopped, I repeat the same process. Using the inhalation and exhalation technique, I was able to do this exercise faster (within twenty seconds) because the conscious is occupied, thereby preventing it from interfering with the subconscious. There is a delicate balance where the danger of doing this exercise too fast meant that I would miss a breath, forget to acknowledge an exit or engage with the arbitrary number, whereas engaging too slowly would allow the conscious to express itself. Therefore, I recommend that the reader finds their own pace while avoiding the above. It is not necessary to imagine the roundabout vividly, but you need to get some sense of it being there. With practice and preparation, Automatic Writing can become smooth and quick.

Sometimes when we write automatically, we might forget the last few words that come out. You must then only write down the words you are sure of and then repeat the Roads and Roundabouts exercise once again. Automatic Writing should start from where you left off, ensuring the Automatic Writing goes in the direction intended by the subconscious and not the conscious.

Typically, trauma may create a barrier between the subconscious and the conscious, as the conscious may be reluctant to allow fearful emotions and memories to come up to its level and be acknowledged. The robustness of the Roads and Roundabouts exercise ensures that the conscious is prevented from expressing itself, which is crucial when recovering from tinnitus. This is achieved by distracting the conscious with inhalation and exhalation, which also serves as a reminder to the subconscious that there are several directions from which to choose. While the conscious is distracted, the subconscious is free to take any exit it wants, hence Automatic Writing. Using this method guarantees pure subconscious expression bypassing the conscious.

The Left And Right Hemispheres Of The Brain And Their Relationship To The Subconscious

The left hemisphere of the brain is concerned with coherence (i.e. things making logical sense); for example, we understand that one plus one is two. However, the flaw is that we can only make as much sense as our database allows. The price of too much logic devoid of emotion is emotional emptiness. This could have been why the tinnitus in my left ear was associated with the right hemisphere, which concerns itself with emotional acknowledgement and feeling. In a pilot study by R. R. A. Coles in 1984, who was the Deputy Director & Coordinator of Clinical Studies at the MRC Institute of Hearing Research at the University of Nottingham, he found that those with tinnitus are more likely to experience it in their left ear.[128] The left hemisphere may have suppressed the right, albeit metaphorically. This may be why the Roads and Roundabouts exercise works clockwise but not anti-clockwise. Gilligan supports this point;

> "...the left hemisphere can and too often does ignore the right and act as if its own maps are the only realities that exist. This can be disastrous, as the functionally isolated left hemisphere has glaring weaknesses. For example, it has only partial and indirect experience of the body (and thus the natural world), it represents only its own position (both visually and cognitively), and it prefers non-living things over living presences."[129]

The left ear or the connection from the left ear connects to the right hemisphere, which is more about creativity and emotion; it is not involved in cognitive function or lateral thinking. Going clockwise rather than anti-clockwise around the roundabout may prevent the left hemisphere from temporarily functioning, implying that the Automatic Writing that comes out must be from the right hemisphere associated with emotion. It suggests the lateral and logical part of the brain is more assertive than the emotional part, but not in the case of Automatic Writing.

This is accurate in its description of the way tinnitus made me react; due to my emotions being out of bounds and in the subconscious, I would respond to highly emotional situations with control and logic, while not being able to access and feel emotions even when there was a need for their involvement. This may be because while the emotional reaction to trauma is kept hidden in the subconscious, the conscious creates a barrier between itself and the subconscious to protect itself from the trauma of the past in the moment. While this is a temporary mechanism for most people, if this continues to happen over a long period, this barrier endures.

The purpose of the roundabout is to stop the conscious from temporarily functioning when we undertake the cycles of breaths by distracting it. This is further encouraged when we go around the roundabout anti-clockwise, temporarily stopping the conscious from functioning. When we have gone around the roundabout once, this reminds the subconscious that there are several different exits from which to choose. At this point, when we stop the exercise, the conscious does not know which exit the subconscious has chosen. However, this is of no consequence since the subsequent Automatic Writing is from the decision of the subconscious made below the conscious awareness.

Preparation For Automatic Writing

Be consistent. When I first practised Automatic Writing, I wrote at the same time each day so that my subconscious became accustomed to revealing itself daily. The environment in which I wrote was quiet and calm, which was essential during this process.

Do not peek. Make sure that the pen is in contact with the paper and that the paper is hidden from your view. For those who can use a pen, avoid looking at the paper or the pen; you may use a cloth to cover the writing hand. If you prefer a computer, it would be advisable to make the writing window extremely small, so only a few words are visible at a time.

Relax mentally and physically. The first time I tried Automatic Writing, the lights were turned off, and I relaxed for a few minutes to slow down my conscious thoughts. Over the next few years, I learnt how to encourage the subconscious to reveal information buried so deeply that it was forgotten at a conscious level and was virtually impossible to retrieve in its entirety. This meant that bits were left in the subconscious, which was why the tinnitus would remain loud. However, with Automatic Writing, it was possible to access all the emotions that were the cause of tinnitus in the moment.

Sometimes, writing one sentence automatically was enough to reduce the tinnitus from 4 to 1, as in the example below. This may be because the particular sentence encapsulated the issue that my subconscious wanted my conscious to acknowledge.

From under the ground came a thought the thought turned into a tree and that tree was me you see and how can that be for all to see

It does not matter if the Automatic Writing does not make sense consciously since the primary goal here is to give the subconscious a mode of expressing itself. The Roads and Roundabouts exercise can be done in conjunction with several Automatic Writing exercises, which are explained in the next chapter.

Clean Language

Before I explain the different Automatic Writing exercises and the method of Focusing, it is helpful to provide some information on Clean Language since this is used in all but one of the exercises.

What is Clean Language?

The late David Grove, a New Zealand-born psychologist, invented the method of using Clean Language with his clients. In essence, Clean Language is a form of questioning, using minimal words and removing any ambiguous language from a question, allowing the person to respond from a deeper source than the conscious. Clean Language encourages my subconscious to explore unresolved issues; unambiguous questioning does not restrict it to responding in a limited way, as it might do if the questions were loaded. I found a way of making the conscious a facilitator to help the subconscious to express itself without the conscious interfering. Journalist and author Judy Rees and Psychologist Alexandru Ioan Manea comment on David Grove's development of the Clean Language concept;

"Clean Language is a precision technique for discovering, exploring and working with people's own personal metaphors. When someone thinks or expresses something in terms of another concept, we consider it to be a metaphor. For example, expressions such as "under the weather", "over the moon" and "in a spin" count as metaphors. The person is not located literally speaking at a place higher than the moon - the metaphor is often the most natural and easy way to convey a meaning."[130]

179

Angela Dunbar, who coaches people on their professional and personal lives using 'Clean' techniques through The Clean Coaching Centre, comments that clean language "...takes the view that the answer required to bring about self-directed change originate from within the person making the change, and not from anyone else."[131] This is why using clean language can be a powerful method for getting to the heart of what you are feeling, even if this feeling is buried in the subconscious. Therapists and coaches may inadvertently bring their perspectives to their clients, which does not always guarantee the subconscious revealing itself; Clean Language provides a solution. Wendy Sullivan is a specialist international trainer of Clean Language, and Judy Rees is a virtual facilitator, trainer and coach. Their book on this subject suggests that, as a complete approach, Clean Language can be combined with the metaphors a person uses, creating a bridge between their conscious and unconscious minds. The connection between the two can become a profound personal exploration: a route to a deeper understanding of themselves, transcending limiting beliefs and behaviours and resolving and healing. The person asking Clean Language questions gets a new understanding of people and even the nature of consciousness.[132]

Most of the Automatic Writing exercises described in this book begin with one or more Clean Language questions; this helps the subconscious to prepare for the exercise ahead. David Pincus and Anees A. Sheikh, academics who have researched Grove's techniques, write that, "The aim of all questions, scripted or improvised, is to objectify the bodily experience within a metaphoric container, to separate the metaphor from the patient through the clean use of pronouns like "it," and to give the metaphor a specific location in the body."[133]

This process is not about communicating with another person or yourself but engaging the metaphor directly. As we know, through communicating with the subconscious, any of our past selves can talk to us in the present (Metaphors are the domain of the subconscious, which is why dreams are comprised of metaphors, which will be explained later). The aim is to lease with oneself from the past to discover the owner of the metaphor. For example, if you discover that the metaphor is a knot, it is essential to communicate with it as if it is a person. After all, this kind of metaphor is generated by the subconscious because it reveals an important message. As with a metaphor in a dream, a metaphor that appears in Clean Language questioning is within a person's memory and can be thought of as a container of information that resembles a foreign invader.[134] An advantage of this approach is that it is unnecessary to discover the trauma directly. Working with metaphors makes this possible, which is advantageous if you are undertaking this process without a therapist. This is because the traumatic memory is surrounded by the metaphor regarding the conscious. (An example of how I have formed a metaphorical story to help a subconscious resolution is on p. 185) Clean Language questioning (explained below) is an effective way of rediscovering trauma. However, before trying the exercise, I recommend reading the following few pages, which explain the process in detail and the practical application of Clean Language Questions.

Clean Language Questions

Clean Language questioning is particularly effective in uncovering trauma in the subconscious since trauma might be represented as a fractured set of metaphors in the subconscious. Later, I explain how Clean Language questioning is used in Automatic Writing. Below is a list of questions formulated with David Grove's Clean Language principles. As we will see, there is no ambiguity, assumption or unnecessary language, which makes it easier for the subconscious to respond.

Is there a feeling?

Does it have a size?

Does it have a shape?

Does it have a colour?

Does it have a texture?

Does it have a location?

Is it more on the inside or the outside?

Does it have a movement?

Is there anything else about it?

What's it like? (probing for a metaphor).

And what happens next?

What would you like to have happened?

Give me an example, is there a feeling?

Chapter 11

Automatic Writing Exercises

This chapter includes six Automatic Writing exercises and describes how they enabled me to unlock memories, thoughts, feelings and emotions that were once hidden and out of bounds to my conscious self. As discussed on p. 173, it is possible to produce Automatic Writing using Roads and Roundabouts. The following exercises use Automatic Writing in several ways, adding variety to my daily practice and encouraging the subconscious to express itself in various written ways. A specific exercise might be more appropriate on a particular day than the others. For example, I refrain from using punctuation when writing automatically because using punctuation is primarily a conscious act; this may inhibit the writing produced by the subconscious. Unlike Dream Analysis, where it is beneficial to analyse dreams, Automatic Writing does not necessarily have to be analysed since it is enough that the subconscious has produced the writing.

I take steps to avoid conscious interference when I write automatically, like using meaningless symbols instead of words that have meaning to the conscious. I keep a piece of paper visible with many arbitrary symbols that do not have emotional associations (so no particular symbol signifies anything to the conscious). For example, a heart symbol is consciously associated with love, which is why it is not used. Instead, I arbitrarily chose symbols like a square, a diamond, a cross, a triangle, a star, a club, and others. In a separate place on another paper that is hidden from my view, I have the same symbols, but each symbol is randomly assigned to an exercise. I begin each exercise (apart from the regular Automatic Writing exercise) with a variation of Automatic Writing. When I want to do Automatic Writing, I pick a symbol that is on display because the symbol is one step away from making a decision using my conscious. Sometimes the suggestion of what symbol to use would come from the subconscious using Focusing or My Dream Analysing Friend (see p. 257).

Most of the exercises below include my name as Sophia, which subtly reminds the subconscious, not the conscious, that it is time to engage in the exercise. Your subconscious may come up with a name it identifies with or prefers not to. In either case, this is not an issue so long as the subconscious is free to express itself. The description of colour in the introduction to the exercises outlined in this chapter originates from the Dream Lexicon, and even though I consciously forget the definitions, my subconscious remembers. Clean Language (explained earlier on p. 179) is used to write the questions for the subconscious to respond to in all the variations of Automatic Writing except in regular Automatic Writing. I have used the Clean Language method in constructing questions to maximise the opportunity for the subconscious to express itself.

Starting An Automatic Writing Exercise

I begin each exercise (apart from the regular Automatic Writing exercise, Conscious Encouraging Dialogue, and the Russian Doll Exercise) by reading the introduction, which sets up the exercise subconsciously. The introduction is the same each time I do a particular exercise because it helps the subconscious prepare for a familiar occurrence of expression. After reading the introduction, a few questions are asked in a similar manner. For all but the final question of each exercise, I respond by using Focusing (Focusing is explained on p. 208). The last question is responded to using Automatic Writing. The first questions set up the scenario, further explored in Automatic Writing, providing a framework for the following Automatic Writing so the subconscious can easily explore the emotion within the context of the responses to the initial questions.

Conscious Encouraging Dialogue Exercise

I have adapted the work of David Grove to form a set of questions (outlined previously) that use Clean Language, and I use these in conjunction with Automatic Writing. I act as my own psychotherapist, and it is important not to analyse the Clean Language exercises but to read through them and acknowledge all that has been written. On completion of an exercise, the subconscious requires time to process the narrative in the coming moments, hours, or days and should be allowed to do this without conscious interference. In the example below, I first felt a butterfly stuck in my chest; of course, this was a metaphor for an emotion of transformation that was trapped and could not develop to move forward. I used a metaphor that I thought of consciously (the butterfly in my chest) to solicit subconscious metaphors and help the narrative move forward into resolution. I used my name, Sapna, as my conscious part, guiding the conversation using Clean Language questioning. In the exercise below, there are five voices. However, when I typically undertake an exercise, I only begin with the part of me, Sapna, my conscious self. It is only after the exercise is completed that I go back through it, and while reading back, I work out who is speaking at any time, which is when I can put their names by their words. It is important to add the names of the speakers after the exercise is complete so as not to influence the narrative, Automatic Writing, or the speaker.

It is necessary to respond to the last 'voice' from the subconscious, which uses Automatic Writing to communicate. The example below is about a butterfly trapped because the door is closed. I consciously guided the conversation for the door to open and for the butterfly to escape by addressing first the butterfly, then the door, and then the hinges and oil for the door. As Sapna, I responded to what had been written automatically and facilitated the direction of the questioning to arrive at a solution by the subconscious. It is a process where I need to wear two or more hats, but there is often a subconscious shift to a resolution which should be achieved with gentleness and care. I am likely to do this exercise when I know the outcome that I desire, in which case this exercise is led by the conscious, which guides the subconscious to work out a resolution.

Example

Sapna: *Stuck butterfly in my chest, is there a feeling?*

Butterfly: I want to escape now Sophia because I will die right here in your chest can you help me please Sophia

Sapna: Escape, is there a feeling?

Escape: I want to escape now I want to run out the door now but the door is closed now I can not open it now

Sapna: Door, is there a feeling?

Door: I am stuck now I cannot open as wide as a house for my hinges are broken I'm shut now but can you open me please Sophia

Sapna: Hinges, does it have a movement?

Hinges: No I'm tight

Sapna: Oil, can you cover the hinges? Is there a feeling?

Oil: Yes I can cover those hinges too I'm door now I will let the butterfly out I'm butterfly now I will follow my own destiny please end this Automatic Writing here now Sophia.

Even though this dialogue is simple and childlike, it is designed to work at the subconscious level. The metaphors guide the subconscious from identifying a problem to a resolution arrived at through the narrative.

You may not understand the meanings behind all of the metaphors, but this should not be of concern, since the process of repair occurs below conscious awareness. The conscious and subconscious work together to support and direct this story. In this dialogue, the butterfly is a metaphor for an emotional part of me which was trapped, and it was possible to release it through this exercise.

Introduction To The Dialogue With Denial

As mentioned, the Denial of my emotions would make the tinnitus louder. So I had to overcome this. Denial, both at a conscious level and a subconscious one, was complex and challenging to navigate. I constructed dialogue with Denial similarly to the above. I have provided a summary of this dialogue below to make it easier for the reader to understand, while the actual dialogue is in the Appendix on p. 335. This dialogue aims to make it possible for Sophia to escape after being imprisoned by Denial. Of course, this is a metaphor for my emotional wisdom being trapped in the subconscious, because of my denial of them. The emotions start with a capital letter to reinforce the notion that these parts are identifiable emotional parts of me by naming them. This makes having a dialogue with them (with the parts that make up my internal conflict) easier because every part is a metaphor. David said how I handled the impasse with 'Denial' was sublime. Gilligan has a delightful mantra: *Make space for all conversations.* David mentioned that my dialogue with 'Denial' was the best example he has seen of living this mantra. As I observed, his Wisdom has been hugely influenced by Stephen Gilligan. The late David Grove had his own mantra regarding working with challenging aspects of our psyche, which was to *"get them to confess their strengths."* This is a truly generative idea, precisely what I did with 'Denial', which exemplifies how I explored my subconscious with curiosity, compassion, and appropriate fierceness, making space for all conversations. I let the process unfold to teach me how to be in a relationship with my Self. In other words, at a conscious level, I am in the Executive role (and quite rightfully), but the Executive cannot and should not attempt to 'push the river'. The dialogue with Denial is an example of how it becomes possible to engage with different subconscious parts for a specific objective.

Dialogue Summary

Sapna offers Denial the sweet of Approval, which he enjoys, making him less powerful. Even though this made him unwell the first time, Denial then tries the sweet of Agreement (The sweets help to narrow the gap between the conscious and the subconscious because they are verbs that alter the different metaphorical parts of the subconscious). After this, Denial says Sophia is ready to come up to the surface of the conscious and out of the cave. Sapna then offers Denial the sweet of Sanction, which gives Denial permission to acknowledge how he truly feels, whether good or bad. Denial insists on not giving up Sophia, but Sapna challenges him to consider what Wisdom wants because Wisdom does not want Denial. Sapna makes the case to Denial that if he denies Sophia's Wisdom, which is the reason that Denial cannot have Sophia because this is a paradox. Denial now understands this paradox and asks Sapna for advice because he does not know what to do. This is a turning point because Denial realises that denying the Wisdom of Sophia is impossible. Sapna agrees that this paradox cannot exist, but if Denial forces this paradox, there will be emotional unrest. Sapna suggests that Denial should be open and accepting of the Wisdom of Sophia to break this paradox. Denial finds this paradox challenging to contemplate. Sapna is sympathetic and supports Denial while reminding him that he

189

cannot hold on to Sophia and must relax into the paradox to untie this metaphorical knot. Sophia finds the courage to stand up to Denial because of Sapna's effort to confront him. This is when the gap between the subconscious and the conscious closes behind Sophia as she escapes from Denial into the conscious. This is how I bring my subconscious Wisdom into the conscious. Sophia acknowledges the work of Sapna and does not forgive Denial for holding her prisoner.

With Sophia's newfound freedom, she tells Denial what she thinks of him and his injustice towards her. Though Denial still hangs on to the hope that Sophia will live with him again, by this point, even he acknowledges this is unlikely. Sapna asks Sophia to remove Denial's ring, which Sophia has already done to make the connection between Sophia and Denial weaker since a ring symbolises commitment. This is how the gap between the subconscious and the conscious shrinks, but it is not narrow enough yet for Sophia to cross over into the conscious; hence Sapna begins talking to Denial again to make the gap smaller. Denial is still reluctant to grant Sophia permission to go, but Sapna reminds him that Sophia does not need his permission. Denial says no one has stopped or challenged him, which is why he still believes he can do what he wants. Similarly, in the physical world, people generally overlook Denial, even though he is right under their noses. (I decided to end the day's dialogue and continue it the following day.)

(The next day, my tinnitus was loud, and I assumed it was because it needed to process the emotional narrative so far) I told Denial that I could not understand him in the form of tinnitus, so he should come and talk to me, and I gave him the floor. Denial explains in a monologue that he has completely transformed now and is flying away while acknowledging that he has grown faint and has distanced himself from

190

Sapna. With Denial gone, Jack wants Sapna and Sophia to make room for him and acknowledge him as their man. He reminds them of their responsibility to turn him into a man with physical form by Sapna finding a man in the physical world to love her. Sapna acknowledges what Jack says and tells other emotional parts to leave her alone because she has an important task ahead. Sapna also calls other parts that might be hidden in the subconscious to make themselves known so they can have a discussion in the light. This ensures that no emotional part remains concealed in the subconscious, which may cause tinnitus. Sapna asks these parts to line up before her and introduce themselves since she wants to know their role in her life and whether they now want to rest permanently or if they have more to teach her. This is how the subconscious is encouraged to get rid of redundant emotions while acknowledging those that are useful to me.

Denial's child comes from Hope and gives Sapna a gift of Love; Hope turns into a candle that guides the way but does not want Revenge. Edifying Fire makes itself known, and its responsibility is to warm Sapna up emotionally and to teach her to emotionally unwind. Desire is next to introduce herself to Sapna by letting her know she needs a partner in the physical world. This part of me narrates their experience so far and their relationship with Sapna. Finally, Desire tells Sapna that the Fire wishes to burn out of control, which is the correct way to feel Desire.

Russian Dolls Exercise

I used the pictures of Russian Dolls by putting them side by side in the order of large to small, labelling them from 1 to 12.

And	Like	And	I	My	My
the	a heavy	I cannot	cannot	subconscious	period
storm	burden	discuss	abide	is	I dread
broke	on my	this	the	wrapped	it because
against	mind it	with	time	up in	my
my	would not	anyone	of the	chains	tinnitus
lonely	let me	other	month	and in	becomes
shore	unwind	than you	because	vain	uncontrollable
It was	and I am	David	it	I was	
too	trapped	because	reminds	put out	
much	in this	it is	me	in the	
for	barrel	too	of what	rain	
me	of hell	much	I have		
to	where	for me	done		
bear	I do not	to			
that	feel	bear			
people	well				
did not					
care					

Under each doll, I wrote automatically by doing the Roads and Roundabouts exercise three times per doll. The writing that unfolded was able first to explain an emotional issue and explore this in-depth with every subsequent doll.

And you know David why I am so full of woe because it is a heavy burden for me to bear when I have nothing else but you pulling me through

The emotions get heavy on my plate as I live in this world alone and at the time of the month nobody understands that I need a man to hold my hand

And I feel like there are chains around my neck making me numb inside like I have done something wrong but I have not

Because I want to burst through the ceiling of life and I have it all my way because I am locked up in a barrel of hell where I am not well

I feel down trodden and desperate to be free and that is what amazes me that people do not understand how much I struggle to live my way

That is why I would not obey them and their way because they make me in dismay today and I want to be free to follow my destiny

Resources from the Present to the Past Exercise

Hypnosis allows us to repair our emotional timeline when we have experienced traumatic events but may not have had the emotional resources to manage them. Gilligan proposes three primary ages of life; the psychological age at the time of the symptom or trauma, the present age and the age of the neglected self.[135] When one part of our emotional self has the ability to connect with another, Gilligan states, we are able to hold multiple versions of ourselves, making transformation possible.[136]

The following exercise is about returning to give the younger version of myself (the neglected self) emotional resources to cope with whatever emotional difficulty she has in her present, which is my past. This subconsciously disrupts emotional trauma from the past by delivering the right resources for what the younger me needs. Even though my past is set in stone, it is still feasible to give a younger version of myself the emotional tools I lacked at the time. In effect, this exercise signals the subconscious to go back to a time of emotional pain and decide what metaphorical object is needed to repair whatever went wrong emotionally for me. The younger me should decide what she needs for herself, rather than myself in the present, giving her something that I feel would help her.

I start this exercise by reading the introduction in bold below, which prepares the subconscious by setting up a familiar scene for it to follow. The introduction to the exercises enables the subconscious to set up a structure for the time in my life that needs emotional repair. Next, I read the questions, pausing for a moment or two after each question and responses become apparent using the Focusing method. Again, I responded to the final question using Automatic Writing, allowing the subconscious to explore further the particular events that took place. In the introduction to the exercise below, I refer to myself as Sophia, which gently reminds the subconscious that it needs to engage with this exercise. The description of nouns and their colours are essential as, once again, these are the same as in the Dream Lexicon, making the metaphors familiar to the subconscious.

Exercise

I as Sophia, walk through an azure blue door into my past. I wear a turquoise t-shirt and a light clear yellow pair of trousers. The bag I carry is pale blue on the outside and emerald green on the inside. My hair is long and blond, and my skin is white. Behind the door are many other doors, with years written above them from 1972, the year before I was born, stretching out into the present of 2020 and into the future. I have a light pink bubble around me which protects me from any negative and harmful emotions I may encounter throughout my journey.

My bag, even though small, contains absolutely everything I need for this journey, my journey. Even though I cannot change the actual events of my past, behind each door is a younger me. I now meet a younger version of myself and give her gifts from my bag, giving them the emotional resources they need to face whatever emotional challenges they encounter. I invite them to look into my bag of immense resources and to take whatever they need. They also let me know about what they experience when they use these resources in their future, my past.

Questions to answer using the Focusing method.

The year of the door I now enter, is there a feeling?
Hello Sophia from [year stated in response to question 1], does what you need have a location in my bag?

Automatic Writing should be used to respond to the next question.

Sophia, what happens next?

Here is an example

Q. The year of the door I now enter, is there a feeling?
A. 1975, 1976 and 1977. (There is usually one year that comes to mind at this stage, but sometimes there can be multiple years, as with this example. This may mean that the event that the subconscious wishes to repair took place over multiple years.)
(I insert the response from the previous question into the next question.)

Q. Hello Sophia from 1975, 1976 and 1977, does what you need have a location in my bag?
A. It is a rubber, and it is at the top of your bag.

Q. Sophia, what happens next?
(I use Automatic Writing to respond to this question.)
A. And when life goes one way I go the other and memories of the past linger on my skin I rub them out like a schoolgirl writing in her new book understanding where she went wrong along life's way mistakes are meant to be learnt from for I will not come down this path again and I

know what I have done wrong please end this Automatic Writing now Sophia you have done enough today.

I used Focusing to answer the first three questions, while the final question was responded to by using Automatic Writing. In this example, the subconscious has identified that things went wrong emotionally between 1975 and 1977, which is why the younger me has chosen a metaphorical rubber to rub out the emotional mistakes of my past. Even though this appears simple and superficial, it is designed to work below the conscious awareness as with all the Automatic Writing Exercises. It does not matter if I had no conscious awareness of what happened at this time or what was being rubbed out. My subconscious constructed the metaphor of the rubber to erase emotions that it identified as negative or problematic. Once again, this process works below the conscious level, and sometimes the tinnitus reduces in volume straight away, while on other occasions, the same effect might take longer; overnight where dreams can kick-start this process. The same principle applies to the following Automatic Writing exercises.

Banned Books

This is an important version of Automatic Writing since it uses the concept of emotional information that was once emotionally banned by my conscious. My tinnitus developed due to my conscious policing itself, deciding what was worthy of acknowledgement on a conscious level. Some of the emotional storylines from my past were forbidden on purpose. This exercise transforms the concept into a section of a library that was once out of bounds but is now accessible to encourage the subconscious to explore this area.

The introduction explains that the books are not only about me but have been written by me. This is important because, as described previously, trauma is constructed by other people's perceptions of me, but I have wrongly identified as originating from me. This is why I specifically ask for information from the metaphorical book I have written in this exercise, ensuring that whatever is expressed in Automatic Writing is not adulterated mistakenly by the perceptions of others.

There is a section in my library called BANNED BOOKS, but this is available to Sophia. It is in the centre of the Library. An enormous red arrow is suspended from the ceiling, pointing to this section. It reads 'BANNED BOOKS LOOK HERE. Everything you should have known but was banned, is available here and now.' I, as Sophia, now enter the beautiful library where every book on the many bookshelves is written by me and about me. Here, in my library, I now wander amongst the bookshelves and browse the many titles available. After some time, my eye catches one book.

Does the book have a feeling?

Does the book have a sense of where you need to look?

Do you have a sense of what the book says?

Example

Does the book have a feeling?

At first, I thought the cover is of silver, but it is gold. The title is written in white on a black panel on the binding and on the front, and it reads, 'You are nearly there Sophia, nearly there now'

Does the book have a sense of where you need to look?

Page 1

Do you have a sense of what the book says?

Now Sophia when the land is dark and sky is grey you cannot be in dismay today because Sophia there is one thing I must tell you for tonight your light will shine brightly for all to see and I'm a man Sophia and you are a woman too you know and together we will grow for I planted your seed a long time ago and there is no going back turning back time again and the tinnitus you hear in your ear today will not be there tomorrow okay but you have heard this a million times before haven't you but I'm Jack you see the man inside waiting to be free please end this Automatic Writing now Sophia you know I'm right all the time.

Variations of Banned Books Exercises

The same set of questions from Banned Books was also used for other Automatic Writing Exercises called Books of Love and Books of Joy. These had the same introduction and questions, but the term 'Banned Books' was replaced with 'Books of Love' and 'Books of Joy'. Again, this allowed the subconscious to explore other aspects and provided a different dimension to what it expressed.

Wise Being Exercise

This exercise was recommended by David and enables specific helpful parts of the subconscious to express themselves by providing advice and resolutions. This exercise asks the subconscious to create three characters metaphorically; the Protector, the Healer, and the Wise Being, each with their purpose and ability.

Protector – who teaches and helps us to maintain appropriate boundaries, asserting our rights and needs in ways wholly respectful of us and others. The Protector also helps to illuminate those areas where we undermine ourselves and gently helps us to take the right action.

Healer – who enables us to journey into the depths of our being, below conscious and subconscious thoughts and feelings, to the deeper unconscious thoughts and feelings that generate the subconscious and conscious thoughts and feelings. The Healer allows us to meet our unhealed wounds (all at the right time and pace) and bring emotional healing to these.

Wise Being – who allows us to tap into the wealth of the collective unconscious and helps us listen to our intuition (inner tuition) and gut feelings. The Wise Being also enables us to see and live according to our unique life path (always a Path with a Heart).

Of course, the descriptions of the three allies are only sketches, and each ally will teach you more about his/her/its nature in due course.

Exercise

Take a flight of ten steps down. With each step, you become more inner-focused, relaxed, and comfortable. (Once again, I use the Focusing method to respond to the first five questions, and Automatic Writing is what I do for the final question.)

Find yourself in a corridor and see a door which is closed at the moment. Does the door have a feeling?

In your own time, open the door (or have it opened for you) and step into the 'holding room' beyond the door; this room can be as plain or exotic as you wish. This holding room, what is it like?

See three more doors, each labelled with the name of a powerful inner ally. What happens next?

When I open the door, do I see the Protector, the Healer, or the Wise Being? Is there anything else about it?

What happens next?

Example

Take a flight of steps (10) down. With each step, you become more inner-focused, relaxed, and comfortable.

Find yourself in a corridor and see a door which is closed at the moment. Does the door have a feeling?
The door is there, but it is invisible like it blends into the background

In your own time, open the door (or have it opened for you) and step into the 'holding room' beyond the door; this room can be as plain or exotic as you wish. This holding room, what is it like?
I am in a room with four walls, a floor and a ceiling but these are transparent and the room is in a jungle. I simply see the outline of the room but I see the jungle.

See three more doors, each labelled with the name of a powerful inner ally. What happens next?
I open the middle door

When I open the door, do I see the Protector, the Healer, or the Wise Being? Is there anything else about it?
The wise being and he is a big brown bear

What happens next?
And well Sophia are you ready to take the last leg of this journey with me you see for I'm the protector and within this room there are four walls but you can't see them and with tinnitus no I think you will never give in for if you give in now you will die and I know you are bound for the sky and what is impossible to some isn't impossible to you and you

know that your dreams have already come true but Sophia in this mellay of madness and rush of the world you stop to admire a dew drop on the spring grass and within the dew drop you will see your destiny in a vision of reality reflected by the sun light in your eyes but with you there is no disguise between good and evil for they were all rolled into one when you went to prison at the barrel of a gun and in your childhood you slept like a child even though you knew that life had wronged you all along and so you slipped into mainstream society quietly and gingerly without acknowledging the pain of belonging to them in their tiny little world and when you entered mainstream society you entered through the back door not announcing your presence to anyone but yourself but you always wanted to stay under the radar Sophia invisible to all but even so in your life you were very small and so Sophia can you take me by the hand and acknowledge that this is actually your land for you belong here and you always had the right to become the human that you were meant to become so celebrate your life but not your diversity is not what you need to do only when people hold you back you know you can fly and while your tinnitus has gone on for 10 years now it's time to say goodbye to it now for this is the last piece of automatic writing that you will ever need to do goodbye Sophia please end this automatic writing now.

Mirror To The Past Exercise

This exercise assists in re-experiencing past events with emotional connections re-established from that time, which may have gone unacknowledged when the experience happened. It also ensures that, as a witness, I am safe from any emotional harm that the events from my past may impose on me. In this exercise, it is possible to reconnect to an earlier age, with the present self by the side, to provide emotional repair and comfort.

Example

I am Sophia, and as Sophia, I can go back to any time in my past using a mirror to see my reflection. As I look at this reflection of myself, I walk towards it, eventually merging with my reflection while entering the mirror. I have a beautiful light pink bubble around me, and I have now become a witness to my past. Hence, while I witness by seeing and/or hearing what happens around me, this bubble protects me by preventing negative or harmful emotions from entering my emotional field. I learn from what I witness and bring this knowledge into the present, and while acknowledging any pain or negativity, I leave this behind at the end while I once again walk through the mirror into my present, where I am here and now. On my wrist is a watch telling me the time; this is a twenty-four-hour clock, so this is how I tell where I am in my past.

(The time identified in the next question is calculated using the Dream Analysis method of calculating the period of life according to the twenty-four-hour clock on p. 249.)

Is there a feeling to the time on the twenty-four-hour clock?

Does my feeling have a location?

What's it like?

Example

I am Sophia, and as Sophia, I can go back to any time in my past using a mirror to see my reflection. As I look at this reflection of myself, I walk towards it, and eventually, I merge with the reflection of myself while entering the mirror. I have a beautiful light pink bubble around me, and I have now become a witness to my past. Hence, while I witness by seeing and/or hearing what happens around me, this bubble protects me by preventing negative or harmful emotions from entering my emotional field. I learn from what I witness and bring this knowledge into the present, and while acknowledging any pain or negativity, I leave this behind at the end while I once again walk through the mirror into my present, where I am here and now. On my wrist, there is a watch telling me the time; this is a 24-hour clock, so this is the way I can tell where I am in my past.

Is there a feeling to the time on the twenty-four-hour clock?
15:30 when I was 27 years old and approximately 1 month in December 2000

Does my feeling have a location?
In the centre of me

What's it like?

And Sophia don't you realise you have given birth today for your nephew was born on the 17th of December and that's your .125 and I know you have suffered greatly with tinnitus up to now and the mountains were so high you couldn't climb them or so you thought but Sophia you are nearly there now for this is the mountain of silence and silence will come to you now and please you cannot go on like this for this is your day Sophia and your day in hell is nearly over now and I'm truthful I'm being honest with you and so can you hear your tinnitus going down now but yet this is the 3rd day of your period now Sophia not bad hey but in the last dream you had today silence was there by your side and now you want it inside you Sophia and it will come soon one day and take your breath away with its permanency and watch your tinnitus go down now and no more automatic writing today.

In each example (except for the Regular Automatic Writing), the first few questions invite the subconscious to set up a framework where an issue can be resolved emotionally, repaired, or explored using Automatic Writing. As resolution often happens below conscious awareness, these exercises may stimulate helpful dreams to explore further and resolve issues. So the tinnitus may not always reduce immediately, but it often goes down upon dreaming the same night.

Chapter 12

Focusing

This section outlines what Focusing is and explains how to do it. I have adapted the Focusing technique from the late Eugene Gendlin's method.[137] He was an American philosopher who developed ways of considering working with the living process and the bodily felt sense. He also formulated the 'philosophy of the implicit, where the subconscious can tap into a deeper source from which responses emerge. To fully explore the issue in a single Focusing session, I have combined it with the Clean Language and the Automatic Writing methods to complete the exercise.

Throughout the day, demands are imposed on us. The alarm clock intrudes on our sleep, reminding us to wake up because of the fear of being late to work, school or an appointment. Work deadlines might intrude on our private lives because our phones and email constantly keep us connected to others; (this may not be at an emotional level) we are compelled to check our phones numerous times a day. They inform us of things we need to know about or do for family, friends, or colleagues. This lifestyle reduces our ability to follow what is natural to us and to meet the needs of our deeper subconscious selves. This discourages the mind-body relationship, where it is possible to tune into the subconscious to acknowledge it. Gilligan comments, "Mind-body dissociation reigns supreme, with little trust or sense of the potential wisdom of the body, and no direct experiential connection with the world. Is it any wonder that we too often walk around feeling numb, scared, angry, or depressed?"[138]

Gilligan proposes that each of us can move to a generative level where we have the physical ability to tap into our wisdom and get better because of the subtle energy of the mind-body connection. For example, we all have experienced this while holding a loved one, walking in nature, or any other time we are engaged emotionally. Gilligan suggests, "At such times, the body is not experienced as a half-witted ass, but rather as a sensitive intelligence that is the base for all meaningful thinking, acting, and feeling."[139]

While the state of neuromuscular lock keeps emotions fixed and rigid, generative trance dissolves this state, allowing the emotions to become free and fluid. Focusing aims to improve the ability to encounter a felt sense in one's body, and because this feeling is subtle, tuning into it becomes necessary. Gendlin suggests that "A felt sense is not an emotion. We recognise emotions. We know when we are angry, or sad, or glad. A felt sense is something you do not recognise - it is vague and murky. It feels meaningful but not known."[140] It is essential to understand this unknown feeling, which is often so far removed from our conscious thoughts that we may not recognise it. So, it may manifest as tinnitus, which is why the Focusing method has proved invaluable.

What Is Focusing?

Focusing creates the right conditions for issues to emerge from the subconscious, like a bud waiting for spring. For example, when the water is agitated, mud rises to the surface of a pond. The aim of Focusing is to sit calmly, so the mud settles at the bottom, and only then does it become possible to see what is at the bottom of the pond, as well as your reflection.

What is a Felt Sense, and how do we know when we feel it? Gendlin explains, "A felt sense is not a mental experience but a physical one. *Physical*. A bodily awareness of a situation or person or event. An internal aura that encompasses everything you feel and know about the given subject at a given time - encompasses it and communicates it to you all at once rather than detail by detail."[141]

This is similar to having a vivid and detailed hypnagogia, a mini dream experienced by some during wakefulness (hypnagogia is explained on p. 226). Focusing helps you to locate painful emotions and work through them to find a sense of peace. At this point, my tinnitus usually reduces.

A felt sense is the accumulation of stored information about one specific person, object, memory or experience. For example, when I consciously reflect upon my special needs school, I attribute mostly negative qualities and bad memories to the experience. Information about my school comes all at once in a single felt sense, which also reminds me of the positive times, though rare. A felt sense is not about a dominant emotion associated with someone or something at present. However, the dominant emotion or feeling is the accumulation of the memories made and experiences gained over time. For example, I have some positive memories of my school, but most of it was about suppression. So as I think about the school, the felt sense of suppression will come up consciously rather than the positive memories. A felt sense about my school delivers not only the dominant suppressive emotion but other emotions, like the friends I had there as a young child. This means that I no longer have a selective conscious perspective but a balanced one after Focusing; the school memory is now complete and brought into the conscious. With tinnitus, a complete set of emotions about an event, object, or experience is not realised fully by the conscious, but part of it remains at the subconscious level. By realising the total and complete emotional perspective, the tinnitus goes down. This is the primary aim of Focusing, concerning recovering from tinnitus; as Gendlin notes, "... a felt sense is not an emotion. It has emotional components in it, along with factual components. But it is bigger than any single emotion, more complex - and much less easy to describe in words."[142] The conscious will analyse a feeling to rationalise it away and may deny it because it is too painful.

As the introduction mentioned, this constant process was the main reason I had tinnitus. This means acknowledging the felt sense allows the emotions and feelings to pass through without feeling stuck.

What I experience after Focusing is often a weird and unfamiliar feeling about a situation or an event. This is because what has come up has just arisen from the subconscious, which I had not been able to acknowledge before. As Gendlin writes,

"Where does that odd feeling come from? It comes from two sources: ... the once-hidden knowledge is now available to your conscious mind. You may be able to use it in some rational plan of action for resolving the problem. This can certainly lead to a feeling of relief."[143]

When I used to have tinnitus, I sometimes felt like something was at the tip of my tongue. Normally, this kind of feeling is harmless and may lead to someone feeling curious or even slightly frustrated since they may not be able to fully grasp it at that moment. However, with tinnitus, this feeling of something being there but just out of reach of conscious awareness, would make the tinnitus louder. Therefore, a benefit of Focusing was to enable the complete emotion and its associated memories to be expressed, resulting in the tinnitus going down or disappearing altogether.

How To Focus?

Below is a step-by-step explanation of the process of Focusing; I would advise you to follow it in the numerical order presented, taking care not to miss any steps. As with the process for Automatic Writing, take some time alone when you know you will be undisturbed. The next few steps are outlined using metaphors to provide an idea of the mindset needed.
Be as comfortable as possible; for example, go to the loo even if the feeling is slight, sit comfortably and be mindful of any slight discomfort.
Creating a mindset to encourage problems or emotions to come up to the surface of the conscious without a barrier is essential. So in this step, you need to clear mental space to make room to look at the problems or emotions individually. Ask what problem needs your

attention at the moment and sit with this question until feelings rise to the surface of the conscious. Do not force yourself to identify the problem immediately, but wait with gentleness and curiosity. What may come out may be big or small problems. Visualise these as parcels of different sizes. It is essential to avoid going into analysing these, like not opening the parcels but instead stacking them in the corner of the room. Keep stacking the problems until you feel something; say, "Yes, except for those, I'm fine".

At this point, gaining a global perspective without detailed examination is useful, since this comes later. It does not matter if this process does not make sense at a conscious level since this works below conscious awareness. I usually take a moment to look back at the stack of problems. Even though the problems are still there, I imagine myself sitting in the empty space I have created alongside them. I look at each item and acknowledge what feels bad while giving each item undivided attention. I stop conscious thoughts about the problem from spiralling away on their own; this would be unhelpful here and now.

At this stage, it is helpful to suspend thinking consciously as much as possible, allowing space for whatever needs my attention from the subconscious to come up to my conscious without being blocked. This is important because, as already explained in this book, the conscious can and does put up a barrier between itself and the subconscious. I ask which problem feels the worst right now. I then ask which hurts the most, feels the heaviest, the biggest, the sharpest, and the most prickly, clammy, or sticky. Next, I identify the problem that feels bad according to my definition of bad. When I do this, I wait for a moment or two, and something usually comes up to make itself known.

I take this time to acknowledge the problem non-judgementally. This allows me to see the problem for what it is, not how I perceive it. I ask myself, what does this problem feel like? Or in Clean language, the problem, is there a feeling? I imagine the feeling is in a transparent container; I refrain from opening it, even though it is easy to open the lid. Instead, I do feel and acknowledge its presence. I ask what this container feels like without referring to labels and descriptions. It does not matter if my feeling differs from the one I would consciously associate with the problem. For example, 'prickly' is not usually used to describe a feeling, but if prickly is the feeling that I have right now, it is essential to acknowledge this.

At this stage, the mind may chatter and generally be noisy; this is my mind's way of distracting me. It is, therefore, important to get past and below this level to the problem itself. When I begin analysing the problem, I tell myself that this analysis is for another time, and I return to the task. This aim is to identify a single feeling with many details, just like a symphony, where it is unnecessary to recognise every note to recognise the musical piece. For example, it is natural to consider a person as a whole instead of listing individual characteristics, and this principle should be applied to the problem. This feeling may be uncomfortable, fuzzy and unidentifiable, but I stay with it.

I ensure that the image that comes to mind and the associated word are a perfect fit. If they do not fit exactly, I try another word. It is like the children's game where when something is hidden, the child who has hidden it guides the seeker by saying colder, cold, warm, warmer, hot, hotter, hottest until the object is found. With Focusing, the body guides you. If there is not a perfect fit, I wait for the felt sense to return and try again; this returning felt sense might be slightly different, but that is okay. I wait for the body to stop changing and give it a few minutes. The feeling is like forgetting something but not knowing what; it is an inner taste you cannot quite put your finger on. The mind may arrive at explanations, attempting to rationalise the feeling, but this is not the aim of Focusing, so I usually wait for the thoughts to pass. I wait until the unclear felt sense becomes stronger while being aware of other thoughts and possibilities. I ensure there is room for the unclear felt sense to rise to the surface until it reaches my conscious.

I wait for a shift to occur when the right word, phrase or image ('handle') is found. For me, this metaphorical Handle is something to hang on to even though the complete emotion or feeling is not apparent at this stage and may often feel like a small bodily internal shift. As Gendlin notes, a shift is "...a well-defined physical sensation of something moving or shifting. It is invariably a pleasant sensation: a feeling of something coming unstuck or uncramped."[144] This movement of the feeling of something shifting inside should not be confused with an inner physical movement because it is more like a mental movement, one which I feel in my chest or abdomen. It is difficult to explain this feeling, so I invite the reader to feel it for themselves.

If the shift in the previous step is small, then in this movement, I stay with the unclear felt sense for a minute or two until it gives clarity since one should vividly feel the unclear felt sense. If not, I repeatedly present the handle to myself and ask what the unclear felt sense is. I repeat this since the answer will emerge on the second or third attempt. One of the most critical procedures in Focusing is the ability to ask "open questions". I ask a question, but I deliberately refrain from trying to answer it through any conscious thinking process. This is why using Clean language is essential rather than closed questions. Sometimes it

215

helps to ask one of the two following questions: 1. What is the worst of this? (Or what is the jumpiest thing about all this? If the handle word was jumpy) and 2. What does the felt sense need? (Or what would it take for this to feel OK?).

I allow this new shift to happen without smothering it, even if it asks me for something which I think is unrealistic. I do not put cement on this new green shoot and wait for other felt senses for clarification. If I stop here for the day, I ensure that I have a clear image; that is the very last image up until that point. When I resume Focusing, I consciously recall the image that will transport me back to where I was the day before or where I had ended the previous session. For example, if the word at the end of the last session was "helpless", in the next session, I need to wonder what it is about helplessness and feel the sense to begin the session. Again, I check the felt sense against the word, and if there is no perfect fit, there is no release.

Focusing is a subconscious process, and some of the above steps may not consciously make complete and logical sense. In my experience, it brought the tinnitus down more often than not while delivering insight into why it was loud and providing an emotional resolution at a subconscious level.

The steps above may be hard to follow and might seem overwhelming to some; this is why I have come up with a written exercise below, which incorporates the abovementioned steps, making it easier to understand. This exercise combines the method of Focusing with Clean Language questioning to get a deeper sense of the feeling. Finally, it concludes with Automatic Writing, which helps tie up loose ends so no emotions are left behind in the subconscious, which may cause the tinnitus to become louder. This means that this exercise facilitates the exploration of emotional memory from start to finish and often acts as a catalyst to find an emotional resolution. This resolution may not be what I expect or want at a conscious level, but it effectively resolves the subconscious conflict, often bringing the tinnitus down.

I respond to one question at a time, and after reading each, I wait for the response to come up from a deeper level than the conscious. This is a strong and distinct feeling because the response is something that I do not recognise or expect. This is when the conscious needs to be tuned out, but this is a feeling that is hard to impart to the reader; the reader should be able to feel it for themselves.

Focusing Exercise

Clearing a space (This is where the subconscious makes room for Focusing to prepare for the exercise to follow. I recommend waiting for a moment or two until any thoughts you may have, are cleared away.)

How is my life going?

What is the main thing for me right now?

What else you feel?

Felt sense

Handle (What is the quality of this unclear felt sense?)
Resonating *(Go back and forth between the felt sense and the word like a phrase or image. Check how they resonate with each other.)*
(In this response, I consciously engage with finding a connection between the Felt Sense and the Handle, this is the only part of the exercise where I work consciously)
Asking (What is it, about this whole problem, that makes this quality? [which you have just named or pictured])
Receiving (Receive whatever comes with a shift in a friendly way. Stay with it for a while.) This is when I feel an inner physical shift or movement of something becoming unstuck.
What would be the next step here? Is there a sensation of movement? (Here is when I get a clear sense from my subconscious about the resolution to the issue.)

Write automatically

Example

Clearing a Space

How is my life going?
Like a bat out of hell but I don't know why but the possibilities are endless.

What is the main thing for me right now?
To stay focused on silence.

What else do you feel?
*Happy today, and a bit anxiou*s.

Felt sense
I'm in the centre of it like the centre of the sea where happiness and anxiety are all around me.

Handle (What is the quality of this unclear felt sense?) *Not sure if the tinnitus will go or not.*

Resonating (Go back and forth between the felt sense and the word, phrase, or image. Check how they resonate with each other.)
I have happiness and anxiety around me because I'm not sure whether tinnitus will go or not and it depends on the tide.

Asking (What is it, about this whole problem, that makes this quality? [which you have just named or pictured])
I need this tide to go my way or I will drown again.

Receiving (Receive whatever comes with a shift in a friendly way. Stay with it for a while.)

I don't swim, I float because the tide is taking me to wherever I want to go.

What would be the next step here, is there a sensation of movement?

To wait and see and to enjoy this journey.

Write automatically

And you must enjoy this journey Sophia please end this Automatic Writing now.

Part D - Dreams

Soon after beginning my sessions with David Corr, I realised that I had unexpressed trauma that needed to be dealt with to recover from tinnitus. For this reason, in addition to my regular hypnotherapy sessions, I also began weekly sessions with a psychotherapist. Although complex and challenging, my psychotherapist and I had a good working relationship, and the sessions often drastically reduced tinnitus. It felt good and helpful to have another safe space to explore my memories, emotions, and feelings. Tom Burns, Emeritus Fellow in Psychiatry at Oxford University, explains that "At its most basic psychotherapy involves using an agreed relationship with specific characteristics, involving a trained practitioner and a patient, to obtain relief from emotional suffering."[145]

My psychotherapist constantly challenged my belief system, how I saw myself through the perspectives of others, and how I had come to adopt these viewpoints. Simply talking about what happened in the past, like having an intimate conversation with a good friend over coffee, may not be sufficient to elicit a change. The aim of psychotherapy is for a person to reveal emotions and experiences to a non-judgemental and confidential professional. Often, they have not expressed these thoughts to anyone, and sometimes they may not even have acknowledged them.

221

The verbalisation of experience to a safe and non-judgemental professional often helps memories and emotions to flow from the subconscious to the conscious. Sometimes the psychotherapist needs to work hard to enable the clients to reveal themselves deeply, since it might be hard for them to reach into a space they have put out of bounds. This is how clients unburden themselves from the emotional baggage that may have been weighing them down. In this chapter, I will outline that analysing dreams proved much more successful in treating tinnitus than psychotherapy.

Later on, my psychotherapist confessed to being a mother of a child with special needs, which may explain why she seemed to understand me and what I had been through so well. I found that my sessions with her helped with the noise reduction, but nine months after our first session, she told me that she could no longer see me due to personal circumstances. I was concerned about stopping my sessions and worried about the impact this would have on my mental health and tinnitus. I wondered if there was anything else that might help me. One day, I thought about discovering dreams and their psychological purpose for some unexplained reason. I was surprised at this random thought, but I followed this hunch, which proved fruitful.

Dreams are instrumental for gaining insight into the subconscious because they process emotional information, which helps us become aware of our emotions and their origins. Analysing dreams proved more effective than psychotherapy, which is why I felt extremely fortunate that my psychotherapy sessions had ended. The Dream Analysis method I developed and will explain later is one way I relearned my emotional history and discovered what the subconscious wished to articulate. This method of analysing dreams has been developed and refined over six months. Since it has proved invaluable in my recovery, I am particularly excited to share this with readers.

Psychotherapy helps us see a situation from another perspective, and Dream Analysis does the same. The difference is that in psychotherapy, the therapist provides a new perspective from their point of view, while Dream Analysis gives the perspective directly from the subconscious, making it totally relevant to the dreamer.

Even the most skilled psychotherapists are human, like their clients. They have a limited ability to make sense of their issues, not to mention having the ability to make sense of another's subconscious mind, which is problematic since a person may not be able to bring up issues within the subconscious during the session. According to Montague Ullman, who was a psychiatrist, psychoanalyst and parapsychologist who founded the Dream Laboratory at the Maimonides Medical Center in Brooklyn, New York, "Dreams are intrinsically honest exercises in self-reflection. Honesty of that kind never lets us down."[146] In my case, therefore, Dream Analysis was a better option.

David Corr and I were excited about working with dreams as a potential treatment for tinnitus. I discovered that dreams provided an understanding of the emotional state of my subconscious and how, by realising forgotten emotions, I was able to dramatically improve my well-being. In time, it would give me back some of the quality of life that had been robbed by tinnitus. In contrast to psychotherapy, where one relies on the therapist to interpret, understand and make sense of one's emotional issues, I found that Dream Analysis was far more accurate and effective. Dreams became windows through which I witnessed my subconscious, resulting in the tinnitus decreasing with greater continuity.

Chapter 13

Dream Analysis

This chapter defines dreams and hypnagogia and explains the importance of dreaming. I illustrate the steps of Dream Analysis, using Automatic Writing to reveal emotional messages from the subconscious. You will learn what hypnagogia is and how they, along with dreams, are a method for the subconscious to process powerful emotions from stressful events. It outlines the purpose of dreaming and how dreams aid emotional recovery. Dream Analysis is an effective alternative to psychotherapy since it provides accurate insights into the subconscious, bringing tinnitus down or making it disappear. Dream Analysis offers a method for the conscious to understand messages from the subconscious. This chapter highlights how the subconscious uses metaphorical language in dreams to express trauma, and explains the principles of Dream Analysis to make sense of dreams.

Understanding Dreams

Dreams help us to make appropriate changes in our lives so that the conscious keeps up with the 'self' concept that the subconscious has about how we see ourselves. To one's dismay, the conscious becomes a barrier to the subconscious when it attempts to avoid bringing emotional trauma into the conscious (explained previously on p. 169). Dream Analysis is one way that this can be reversed. Unfortunately, dreams are not perceived in the same light as evidence-based medicine because they are non-reproducible and subjective.

Rosalind Cartwright, Ph.D., is the Director of Psychology at the University of Illinois, College Of Medicine. While researching sleep disorders, she opened a sleep laboratory to study the function of dreaming and REM (rapid eye movement) sleep. She discovered dreams are ideal for re-engaging with memories and emotions that have been forgotten consciously. The reorganisation of memories helps us update our self-identity and recognise what is good and what causes us harm. As far as Cartwright is concerned, "... dreams seem almost like a rehearsal for recovery."[147] She describes a dream as when a,

> "...disturbing waking experience is reactivated in sleep and carried forward into REM, where it is matched by similarity in feeling to earlier memories, a network of older associations is stimulated and is displayed as a sequence of compound images that we experience as dreams."[148]

Dreams differ from other mental simulations because they are enveloping, unlike daydreaming or simply imagining.[149] If dreams are recorded and analysed, this helps the conscious to realise the emotional messages produced by the subconscious.

What is Hypnagogia?

According to Andreas Mavromatis [150], who has a Ph.D. in psychology and philosophy, with an interest in consciousness and has researched other academics, past and present, hypnagogia occurs in around seventy-five percent of people. I discovered that I was one of the majority who could experience hypnagogia, which was tremendously useful in the immediate reduction of tinnitus. Hypnagogia can be thought of as concentrated and intense dream-like imagery, even when the person is awake. As a result of my hypnagogic experience being so intense and depending on the imagery and sound's vividness, it dramatically and immediately impacted the level of my tinnitus. The greater the vividness of the hypnagogia, the more the tinnitus is reduced in volume. Therefore, Hypnagogia are analysed in the same way that dreams are analysed.

Whereas a dream is longer and may have a narrative or at least a defined beginning, middle and end, hypnagogia lasts for just a few seconds whilst awake. They do not have a well-defined narrative structure, but have a unique structure that differs from dreams. This is because it packs the entire message into a few seconds. Different senses detect different aspects of hypnagogia and combine them into one. Hypnagogia is multi-sensory, which means it absorbs all of my attention. The late Arthur Deikman, clinical professor of psychiatry at the University of California, San Francisco, and a member of the editorial board of the Journal of Humanistic Psychology, states that,

> "...sensory translation may occur when (a) heightened attention is directed to the sensory pathways, (b) controlled analytic thought is absent,

and (c) the subject's attitude is one of receptivity to stimuli (openness instead of suspiciousness)... the general psychological context may be described as *perceptual concentration.* In this special state of consciousness the subject becomes aware of certain intra-psychic processes ordinarily excluded from or beyond the scope of awareness."[151]

Hypnagogia presents multiple emotional angles, and, like dreams, it comes from the subconscious to the conscious; this is why hypnagogia is so effective in reducing tinnitus. As mentioned, tinnitus results from emotions being trapped in the subconscious, with no way of allowing the conscious to experience and acknowledge them. Therefore, hypnagogia presents multiple emotional angles of the same issue to the conscious. This differs from when emotions are suppressed, putting the process of suppressing emotions into reverse.

Dreams, Hypnagogia and Recovery

In the initial stages of recovery, when I could sleep, I did not know the benefits of analysing dreams. If I were to experience stress during the day, my dreams would become vivid that night. This was because I had lost the ability to process emotionally-overwhelming stimuli at the conscious level, and as a result, these stimuli manifested in my dreams. After researching the nature of dreams, I realised that dreams are a way for the subconscious to process emotions that result from stressful events. Thus, analysing dreams was vital to recovery. Memory consolidation occurs in sleep, and is a part of the process of dreaming. Nielsen talks about the process of memory consolidation occurring in sleep, which is also when the subconscious processes emotions.[152]

Jessica Payne, a Harvard researcher, suggests that sleep helps us consolidate and recall negative emotional events, which the conscious often edit out. Hence, working with dreams proved to be successful in reducing tinnitus. Cartwright suggests that the subconscious never rests, but uses nocturnal dreams to process our emotional experiences during wakefulness.[153] Realising the benefits of analysing dreams led to Dream Analysis becoming a vital part of my recovery from tinnitus.

Tore Nielsen, a sleep psychiatry academic at the University of Montreal, comments on Cartwright's research; and further explains that Cartwright propounds that dreaming during REM sleep has multiple purposes; dreams regulate negative emotions, formed when waking emotions are strong though not overwhelming, and the emotional tone of dreams shifts from negative to positive throughout the night.[154] In the long-term, it enables us to adapt emotionally to the changing situations that, over a lifetime, make up our self-concept, whereas the short-term function is to improve one's mood.

Clete A. Kushida, is a neurologist who specialises in the diagnosis and management of sleep-related breathing disorders; he comments that REM sleep gives us greater access to memories than slow-wave sleep or wakefulness;[155] hence, dreams occurring in REM sleep prove an invaluable window to understand the emotional response of the subconscious to the past and provide an insight into troublesome feelings. According to Cartwright, the images in dreams are,

> "...formed by pattern recognition between some current emotionally valued experience matching the condensed representation of similarly toned memories. Networks of these become our familiar

style of thinking, which gives our behavior continuity and us a coherent sense of who we are. Thus, dream dimensions are elements of the schemas, and both represent accumulated experience and serve to filter and evaluate the new day's input."[156]

Images in dreams are a constant creative product and result from established subconscious schemas evaluating present experiences. Through Dream Analysis, the conscious can intercept messages that the subconscious produces, which enables the subconscious and the conscious to have the same emotional knowledge stored in the subconscious.

Most people pay little attention to their dreams; thus, this chapter highlights the vital importance of being able to understand them. I would like to share techniques of Dream Analysis that I have developed, as well as explain how and why dreams are crucial for emotional recovery and good mental health. The Dream Analysis explained in this chapter is the culmination of trial and error and refinement. Throughout this book, whenever dreams are mentioned, it is a reference not just to dreams but also to hypnagogia (explained on p. 226) since all of the principles that apply to dreams, can also apply to hypnagogia. According to the late Prof. Michael Aldrich, the founder of the Sleep Disorders Centre at the University of Michigan,

"...most dreams have relatively little concern with unconscious conflict and do not interfere with sleep. Dreams on which emotional conflicts are superimposed, however, are more likely to be remembered. Thus, emotional conflict does not cause dreaming but instead uses dreams as a vehicle to express conflict indirectly."[157]

These emotional conflicts within the subconscious cause tinnitus, which is why understanding them is essential for recovery.

Dream Analysis As A Common Language

The principle of Dream Analysis is to use metaphors to build up a common language between the subconscious and the conscious, which the subconscious produces with dreaming and which the conscious understands. Both the conscious and the subconscious must be aware of one another to develop a helpful and respectful relationship which maintains understanding between the two (explained further on p. 134). Past President and Board Chair for the International Association for the Study of Dreams, Gregory Scott Sparrow, emphasises this point; he notes that Carl Jung's view of the dream image as the product of the "reciprocal relationship" between conscious and unconscious challenges the position that the manifest dream imagery is "strictly determined"... by a wholly unconscious process before observation.[158] The subconscious wants to be understood by the conscious, which is why the subconscious ensures that the metaphors it produces are consciously recognised. Sparrow and Ullman support the idea that; a dream forms because of felt dissonance[159] between the dream ego and emergent content, and as we observe, this interactive interface arises from the dream, from the dream ego and its need to combine with the intruding content renders the content in a specific malleable shape.[160] Later, I make a similar reference to how dreams have a plasticine-like quality where the subconscious can mould dreams into whatever metaphors it wishes.

230

In Ullman's words,

> "...the dreamer, forced to employ a sensory mode, has to build the abstraction out of concrete blocks in the form of visual sequences. The resulting metaphor can be viewed as an interface phenomenon where the biological system establishes the sensory medium as the vehicle for this expression and the psychological system furnishes the specific content."[161]

Dreams are accurate representations of the emotional reality stored in the subconscious. Normally, this process is below conscious awareness and has little consequence for the conscious. As outlined in the Introduction, the goal of emotional recovery is to acknowledge emotional trauma consciously, and Dream Analysis is an effective means of doing this. Sparrow elaborates by reflecting on Jung's perspective,

> "Jung was perhaps the first to articulate the premise that dream imagery derives from the reciprocal interplay of two sources rather than one, when he said that the dream image... is the result of the spontaneous activity of the unconscious on one hand and of momentary conscious situation on the other. The interpretation of its meaning...can start neither from the conscious alone nor from the unconscious alone, but only from their reciprocal relationship..."[162]

The subconscious and the conscious must collaborate to have a common understanding of dream metaphors which may initially arrive consciously. Through dreaming, the subconscious continuously connects experiences of the past and present. By the conscious interception of dreams, it becomes possible to gain an insight into all that is stored in the subconscious. What we learn may be pleasant or painful, so entering the domain of the subconscious is not for those who are emotionally fragile. For me, recovering from tinnitus has outweighed the discovery of any personal trauma; I was prepared for any painful experiences brought to the conscious from the subconscious during the process of Dream Analysis.

Dr Daniela Sieff, whose research interests lie in the dynamics of trauma and healing by interweaving academic scholarship with her lived experience, elaborates further,

> "The language of the unconscious is image and metaphor; dreams are snap-shots of what is happening in the unconscious. Collecting dream images, and working to uncover the impact of the metaphors they contain, is a profound and effective way to explore what has been hidden in the unconscious."[163]

When we sleep, the conscious is dormant, meaning the subconscious has no restriction on how it expresses itself. We can think of the conscious as a gatekeeper to the subconscious, and when we sleep, the gatekeeper becomes inactive.

The primary function of dreaming is for the subconscious to put emotions in their correct place. Dream Analysis allows the conscious to intercept, but not interfere with this process and to learn the source of emotions in the subconscious. So, in this case, the conscious knows where the emotions are and can trace them back to understand where they came from and to know their true nature.

Principles of Dream Analysis

I developed a method of Dream Analysis through trial and error after reading a scientific article on the purpose and function of dreams, which mentioned that,

> "Sleep has also been shown to target the consolidation of specific aspects of emotional experiences, as well as mediate the extinction of human fear memories. By experimentally varying the foreground and background elements of emotional picture stimuli, Payne et al. have demonstrated that sleep can target the strengthening of negative emotional objects in a scene, but not the peripheral background."[164]

At this point, I became curious to discover more about the relationship between dreams and emotions and whether this would help with tinnitus. I learnt that dreaming is a way for the subconscious to process emotions while we sleep; this is like a person who cleans your house while you are sleeping so that you do not intervene in this process. One major part of my recovery was the method I developed of analysing dreams, which made it possible for the conscious to witness while the subconscious tidied up emotions and rediscovered the missing ones. By analysing dreams, it is viable for the conscious to intercept but not interfere with the process to understand what is being tidied away. When this happens, the conscious has the same information as the subconscious, and this common understanding is invaluable in recovering from the emotional trauma that the conscious might not acknowledge. There are several reasons for this. One reason could be that, as in my case, trauma happened in childhood when I did not have the emotional support or sufficient knowledge to understand what was happening to me. Dream Analysis is the recognition of experiences, memories, and emotions that the conscious has forgotten or left unacknowledged. The subconscious can re-explore the past and understand it from an emotional perspective. Nielsen suggests,

> "...emotional balance is achieved during sleep by the reduction of dysphoric emotion through the relating of recent memories with past memories of a similar emotional timbre... It also accounts for why dream experiences become increasingly bizarre across the night."[165]

Dreams helped me understand the events that happened in my past, and I could revisit the important yet unacknowledged emotions. I developed and refined a method of analysing dreams, which enabled the dream's true meaning to be revealed, rather than accepting imposed interpretations, which can be unhelpful to emotional recovery and well-being. This unique Dream Analysis process eliminates the problem of imposed interpretation by others or, indeed, the conscious self. This is why I have avoided referencing Freud or others in his field. Dreams are metaphors for emotional experiences that happen to us. By understanding these metaphors, it becomes possible to understand our dreams. It is vital to keep the metaphors consistent so that the subconscious relies on the metaphors in the dream to be understood by the conscious, creating a common language between the conscious and subconscious.

Making A Written Record Of Dreams

I am unable to use my hands and needed to find a way of noting the dreams down. I tried remembering them until my carer came to write them down in the morning, but it was impossible to remember all of them. I tried a couple of techniques to improve my memory, but I could not remember all the dreams in detail. I knew there would be a good chance of the tinnitus being at one or not there if I could find a way of recording my dreams straight after having them. Fortunately, technology came to my rescue, and I have a computer which I control with the movement of my eyes.

The system comprises of touch screen monitor with an additional panel underneath that has two infrared cameras which recognise and track the eye movements of the user upon the screen. This technology is specifically created for people who cannot use their hands or a traditional computer set-up owing to a physical impairment. A standard system is set up with an alphabet grid with word prediction and a number grid that enables the user to perform basic word processing or use it for communicating with a speech output device. I contacted a person I knew who worked with this technology and explained that I needed to be able to note my dreams down and wondered if there was a way of putting a computer above my bed. To my delight and amazement, he said this was possible and came over to install a system.

It was an exciting day, and Dr Mick Donegan was intrigued to know if it would work to enable me to record my dreams independently. Over the next few nights, when I had a dream or hypnagogia, I managed to type them out using eye-gaze, it was another milestone in my recovery, and from then on, my tinnitus was at 1 or below on most days.

A Certain Amount Of Emotions

For the tinnitus to remain at one or below (the scale of measurement explained on p. 123), I realised that there was a certain amount of emotions that the subconscious needed to produce for the conscious to acknowledge each day because emotional messages needed to be deciphered through Dream Analysis. If the quota of emotions for that night were not expressed in a single dream, the remainder would often form following dreams or hypnagogia (explained on p. 226). In addition, the tinnitus would increase during a vivid dream and often remain loud until the dream was analysed. This was not of concern, since vivid dreams indicated that big powerful emotions were passing from the subconscious into the conscious. However, I realised this was temporary, and that the tinnitus would reduce after analysing the dream, which was particularly noticeable when a dream revealed an issue of major emotional significance. Over the next few days, I would have dreams where this issue was entirely explored, and consequently, this brought the tinnitus down.

Forgetting Dreams

If I forgot a dream, the tinnitus would remain loud, so it was essential to note dreams down as soon as I had them, regardless of how tired I was. When I could not remember any part of the dream, undertaking

Automatic Writing would often reduce the tinnitus during the day. One explanation for this is that the subconscious would express the emotional message of the forgotten dream through Automatic Writing. Sparrow explains that, "Extracting the process narrative thus clarifies a continuous background plot that weaves or "maps"... the metaphoric imagery into a cohesive storyline."[166] I observed a pattern in my dreams where, typically, I would have one dream that would provide an overall summary of my emotional issue. Subsequent dreams explored the same issue but progressively in more depth.

My dreams would explain my past experiences in exquisite detail, connecting them with emotions and how I should have felt about them at the time. My research demonstrates that Dream Analysis is superior to psychotherapy but more challenging because there is no one to hold your hand. It takes bravery to charter the waters of the subconscious, but the rewards are immense.

Some Of The Other Effects Of Dreaming

Until the emotional issue had been completely explored at a conscious level, my tinnitus would remain loud for a few days. Then, when a particular narrative ended, the sound would reduce to 1, and the dreams would move on to another issue. Sometimes I felt tired and unwell while dreaming intensely, but this would be because significant and emotionally intense issues passed from the subconscious to the conscious. This period would sometimes last for a few days or weeks, but I was not concerned. I knew I would feel better after an episode like this, and I realised that the process of dreaming needed to explore my complete history at an emotional level. I consciously realised that this was what my subconscious needed to do, to help the conscious to be a witness as it moved through my emotional narrative.

When my day had been stressful, with unpleasant events, I found that the dreams of the same night no longer explored my past or followed a pattern. Instead, the subconscious would be concerned with resolving and presenting an emotional perspective on the day's events. This could have been because my dreams resolved issues straight away, so it did not add to the backlog of emotions in the subconscious.

Exercise - Plasticine Dreams

We can think of dreams as having a plasticine-like quality because the subconscious can mould them. For example, when I first began recording my dreams, I had up to twenty-five short dreams a night, including hypnagogia. This disturbed my sleep since I had to note them down because my tinnitus would get louder if I did not. I was able to have fewer brief dreams, from up to twenty-five per night to two to five longer, more in-depth ones, making it possible for me to have enough sleep. Before sleeping, I imagined a light blue (Light blue is defined in my dream lexicon as 'creativity and the freedom to break free') conveyor belt between the subconscious and the conscious. Subsequently, I imagined lots of little balls of plasticine which joined together to form dreams that became larger and fewer in number. I visualised that they were put on the conveyor belt, which went from the subconscious to the conscious and made the dreams or the hypnagogia larger and fewer in number. Although I still had to wake up to write them down, I needed to do so less often. Another advantage of bigger dreams was that they were easier to analyse, and I could make sense of them more often, this meant that the tinnitus was more likely to reduce.

Chapter 14

How to Improve Dreaming

This chapter describes how I could develop and refine methods of dreaming through trial and error until they became effective in my recovery.

Walking Down the Stairs

This is one of my favourite exercises which David came up with, and even though it took time and practice to master, it has been worth it. This exercise helps me to go from complete wakefulness to sleep. So I can stop and remain anywhere between sleep and waking. Walking down the stairs is beneficial before undertaking Automatic Writing and if I want to experience hypnagogia (see chapter on Automatic Writing, p. 169 and chapter on Dream Analysis, p. 224). The exercise helps the conscious recede, allowing the subconscious to become more dominant whilst in the waking state.

Exercise

I begin the exercise by imagining that I am lying on a beautiful white cloud, which slowly rises higher and higher into the clear blue sky. In my Dream Lexicon, I define blue sky as an "unlimited emotional space of trust, peace, communication, authority, wisdom, honesty, loyalty, integrity, conservatism, and frigidity". The cloud is strong enough to support me and take my weight completely. As I drift higher and higher into the sky, I become drowsier and drowsier while feeling increasingly relaxed. The cloud takes me to the top of a flight of stairs, and if I wish, I can get off the cloud and walk down the stairs. At this point, I am on the hundredth step at the top of the flight of stairs. I am wide awake and alert. As I proceed down the steps, I count backwards from one hundred with every step taken. There are landings every 10 steps (90, 80, 70 etc.), and I become drowsier as I get farther down the steps. It is at this point that I often experience hypnagogia. I also can write automatically, where the emotions expressed are strong, and the writing becomes deep, which reduces the tinnitus or often makes it disappear altogether. I feel myself drifting towards sleep, which makes it possible to determine my level of drowsiness while maintaining control. I can pause this exercise at any point between wakefulness and sleep to investigate this subconscious level.

Alternatively, it is possible to start at the bottom of the flight of stairs, at step 1, and climb upwards towards step 100. It is good to try this both ways to see what works best for you. Perhaps, you may find that the 'exertion' of climbing the stairs is more helpful in bringing on deeper levels of hypnagogia.

You will find a hallway or passageway at each landing leading off to the

240

left, right, or in both directions. I recommend exploring level 70 for a week, then moving deeper to 60 etc. If you 'draw a blank at any level,' this indicates that more time needs to be spent at the previous level.

Count slowly down from 100 to 90 while saying each successive number with each step-down, and the counting coinciding with each successive out-breath. Check in here and notice the differences, then continue counting down slowly in the same way to 80 and check in again. Continue down to 70 and turn either left or right toward the room of hypnagogia. This slower process may well assist you in experiencing the deeper state you need. When I do this exercise, I stop at each level while doing the Body Relaxation exercise explained on p. 308. This interruption may not be beneficial for some, since they may feel that stopping the 'Walking Down the Stairs' exercise may bring them back to full wakefulness.

The Dream Creation Meditation: An Alternative Exercise

I listened to the Dream Creation Meditation by Jason Stephenson before I slept and wondered if it would help create dreams. In fact, it helped me produce hypnagogia straight away, immediately bringing the tinnitus down.

Please follow this link:
https://www.youtube.com/watch?v=TTGd2TGsBVM[167].

I have provided the text to the meditation below:

Welcome to this dream creation meditation.

Bring yourself into a comfortable relaxed or lying position, or if you're ready to go to bed simply lie on your bed and close your eyes.

Take a nice deep breath in and as you exhale, release it, let it go with a gentle sigh. Allow your awareness to focus on the space in front of your closed eyes.

For a moment just witness this space. What is it that you see in the space in front of your closed eyes?

Perhaps you see colours, patterns or even images, perhaps you just see darkness.

Without trying to alter or change what you see, simply witness it. Consciously clear this space now, making it a blank canvas for your dreams.

Visualise a paintbrush and use this brush to write a message in this space.

Write, "I will remain aware that I am dreaming and create my own dreams."

As you write each word mentally, repeat it, "I will remain aware that I am dreaming and create my own dreams."

What colour paint did you use?

Choose another colour and write it once more, mentally repeating, "I will remain aware that I am dreaming and create my own dreams."
Allow the writing to fade out so that your canvas is once again a blank

space.

You can create any world that you want in this space, you just need to allow the mind to float free.

You are the artist who paints your own dreams, the architect who designs your own sleep reality.

Visualise yourself standing in this space.

See yourself standing and consciously be aware that this is of your own creation.

Look down at your hands and see them in front of you, do this in any way that feels right for you.

Maybe you can see your hands vividly, or perhaps you create a sense that they are there.

Visualise your hands in any way that works for you.

Releasing this image now, and become aware once again of the space in front of your closed eyes.

I will now mention a series of images, and do your best to visualise these in any way that you can.
Visualise a kite flying high in the sky.

A sunset over the ocean.

A goldfish swimming in a bowl.

Footprints travelling over sand.

A waterfall cascading over rocks.

Now letting go of these images, let your own imagination step in.

You are the artist and creator of your own dreams.

As you drift off now, you're in control of your own dreams, and you are the architect.

Let your creative mind float free, and may your dreams be peaceful, safe, and wondrous.

I have a variation of this meditation where I visualise writing numbers against the blackness of my closed eyelids, making the colours of each number vivid; subsequently, I experience hypnagogia.

Describing Dreams

The Dream Analysis method that I developed works by writing a dream down in as much detail as possible, as soon as you have had it. The first step is to ensure that you have a paper and pen by your bed to make a note of any dreams upon waking. In the beginning, it does not matter if this is just a single word, a fragment of a dream, or even a feeling you have. It took me a few weeks before I fully remembered my dreams. If I can only remember a small part of the dream, this is not an issue because I can recall the dream using Automatic Writing if I do it immediately upon waking. However, this only works if I remember a small part of a dream. I only remembered an image in the example below, but I knew there was more to the dream. After writing the first line, which was all that I remembered (written in bold below), I wrote automatically so that my subconscious could describe the rest of the dream. The explanation is analysing the dream using Automatic Writing, which was terrific. If I had not undertaken Automatic Writing, the tinnitus would have remained loud since the dream's emotional message would not have been completely expressed.

A test tube was in a holder with orange at the bottom, light yellow in the middle and white at the top.

"*Someone tipped it out and this is because Sophia your life was an experiment you see and it had gone wrong until you had hypnotherapy and Sophia you can't go on like this and so you tipped it out you see so remember that really you have the power and the control now and it's time to put life together again your way and I want you to do Focusing later on today.*"

So now we have a description of a dream. A method of noun substitution is used to discover what the subconscious has constructed to convey to the conscious. Giving a predefined emotional meaning to nouns in dreams is explained on p. 251.

The Importance of Metaphor Consistency

The subconscious produces dreams by combining metaphors to organise and emotionally process memories and conscious experiences from the physical world, which may not have fully been consciously realised.

As Jerome Bruner, Ph.D., the late American psychologist who made significant contributions to human cognitive psychology and cognitive learning theory in educational psychology, suggests, "We tend to perceive things schematically, for example, rather than in detail, or we represent a class of diverse things by some sort of averaged 'typical instance'."[168] The subconscious organises metaphors to produce typical instances that can be recognised by the conscious. The narrative of a dream may be the combination of unconnected metaphors which the subconscious has combined, delivering a specific emotional message. The recombination of metaphors surpasses the literal meaning of dreams, which we may superficially consider.

Dreams accurately represent our emotional conflicts, which may be about the past, the present, or what we imagine in our future. Dreams are of no importance in our conscious awareness, but they have played a vital part in my recovery from tinnitus; hence, it was essential to bring my dreams up to the conscious level so they could be recorded for analysis. Dreams are combinations of metaphors produced by the subconscious to organise emotional experiences. Sparrow elaborates this; "In light of this age-old conviction, the central task in content-focused dream work has been to view the dream images as "symbols," defined as "any image or thing that stands for something else..."[169]

The method of metaphor consistency rests on the notion that every character or aspect of a dream represents an emotional part of me, and as a result, I can discover the message that a particular part of me is delivering. The characters in dreams simultaneously explore an emotional narrative while remaining true to their identity. I became familiar with these characters over time, making it easier to understand them, which provided me with a greater comprehension of myself. All

246

the elements in dreams are extensions of the emotional self and contribute to why I am the person I am today and my journey along the way. By understanding this, it is possible to gain an insight into the different parts and how they contribute to my subconscious. Once again, nouns are substituted for other nouns, which provide a broader perspective of the original noun and are relevant to my life.

Nouns Within Dreams

Sometimes, the nouns in the dream are recognisable as parts of me, while at other times, they do not resemble me. However, I have no concerns since it is necessary to explore these unrecognisable parts to gain a deep understanding of the aspects that make up the subconscious. Eventually, I built up a lexicon of seven hundred and sixty nouns, each with its own definition. As the lexicon was developed, it became more likely that the nouns in any subsequent dreams would already have a definition in the lexicon. This made the process of Dream Analysis fast and, more importantly, provided greater accuracy, which meant that the tinnitus would reduce in volume with greater frequency after Dream Analysis.

When a noun recurs in future dreams, an emotional description of that term must always be applied to the same noun. Therefore, the subconscious and the conscious need to build a lexicon to associate a particular noun with a particular emotional description. It is necessary to keep an accurate record of nouns and their associations rather than relying on memory since Dream Analysis is a complex process. When done correctly, it gives the conscious the tools to understand accurately what a dream means and, in turn, precisely understand the message from the subconscious.

Chapter 15

Writing a Personal Dream Lexicon

This chapter provides more detail about the actual process of analysing dreams, which remains essential even after the period of Dream Analysis has ended. The first time I record a dream which includes a particular noun, I give the noun a unique emotional description that is personal to me. Noun definitions should be stable, reliable, and personally meaningful, though definitions can change over time with emotional changes. For example, as a dog-lover, if I had a dream about a dog, I would describe this noun as a 'part of me that is friendly, loyal, comforting, lovable, pure and innocent, without emotional restrictions but full of simple emotions and that communicates differently'. If, later on, a dog attacked me in the physical world, and if this changed the way I felt about dogs, the definition in my Dream Lexicon would alter, and the emotional meaning of dogs in my dreams would also change. This emotional description would not be true if someone has other feelings about dogs, in which case their definition would be different, reflecting their impressions towards dogs.

The above description is why it is not wise to help people analyse their dreams if the purpose is for them to understand their subconscious. It is unhelpful to refer to the many books that tell you the meaning of dreams since the definitions within those books have been predefined and not personal to the individual.

Dreams That Specify A Time In Life

I never thought maths was my strong point, but I discovered that my subconscious was excellent at maths. Sometimes my subconscious needed me to acknowledge a specific time when a specific event happened. I discovered this method by accident, and the subconscious has used the same formula to implicate the time in my life that a dream refers to. The subconscious used the time of a 24-hour clock to indicate this and reveal the period of life it refers to; amazingly, it is always accurate. It is the conscious's job to work this out using a standard formula and a calculator.

The formula is: my current age (a) divided by 24 (24 hours), multiplied by the time of day shown in the dream (t). This is because the subconscious has used the 24-hour day to represent my lifetime so far. $(a \div 24) *t$

For example, here is a dream I had when I was 42:
Female voice said, "It's 5:45 on Friday 6th of May. I cannot move. I'm paralysed to the ground ". (Remarkably, It was a Friday on the 6th of May in 1983)

I divide my age (42) by the twenty-four-hour clock and multiply it by the time in the dream: $(42 \div 24) *5.45 = 9.5375$.

We now know this dream referred to when I was nine and a half. To find a more specific date, I can round the fraction to one decimal place (9.5 in this case) and multiply the fraction (only the fraction, here .5) by 1.2. The result is the number of months from my birthday that the event occurred. So as my birthday is in November, .5*1.2 = 0.6, and May is six months away from November.

This dream tells me that I was emotionally paralysed in May 1982. Even though this was quite difficult to work out, it is a big revelation because the dream points to a specific time in my life that I need to acknowledge. This is when my special needs school first suppressed me emotionally (which is why I had emotional paralysis). If I wished, I could have undertaken Automatic Writing to discover more about what the subconscious remembered about May 1982. Although I came up with this formula by chance, it may work for you because by reading about it, your subconscious might absorbed the formula.

Noun Substitution

Alongside building the lexicon, I substitute the nouns within any given dream description with their emotional definitions from the lexicon. I come up with the definitions for nouns with emotional significance by describing the primary function of the noun and giving this primary function an emotional connotation. For example, the word "table" means "an emotional surface", and the word "school" means "emotional learning environment for young parts of me". For instance, even though my school did not have black walls, if I had a dream about my special needs school where the walls of the school were black, this dream would be correct metaphorically. This is because the definition of school is "an emotional learning environment for young parts of me", and the definition of black is "hidden, secretive, unknown, mysterious, powerful, controlling, keeping emotions bottled up". According to this method of Dream Analysis, the emotional experience of my childhood was powerful and controlling, which is why I kept my emotions bottled up. This definition refers to the emotional circumstances of my childhood, which gave rise to the way I am today. I was unaware of this consciously, which may be why, as a child, I experienced emotional trauma. This method of analysing dreams is how we can gain emotional insights to past and present experiences. It is why Dream Analysis was particularly effective in my recovery from tinnitus.

When replacing the original nouns in dreams with their definitions, what may come out may sound slightly unnatural in a sentence. For example, "a small van" could be exchanged for "my small body" in the Dream Analysis. In my experience, dreams are primarily reflections of the emotional state of the subconscious; in a description of a dream, the nouns are not as crucial as the verbs. Therefore, the nouns can be replaced with a description with a broader emotional meaning without altering the understanding of the original dream. Dream Analysis is not about imposing your interpretation on a dream but letting the dream speak for itself.

For example, it is helpful to divide different colours into different emotions since the colour spectrum can represent the emotional spectrum. Colours often make up a vital part of dreams; colour is another tool that the subconscious uses to tell us about different emotions.

Here is an example of Dream Analysis based on a dream I had a long time ago:

Male voice[1] said, "do you know I tick[2] once a day[3]? " another male voice said, "I tick[2] too. Once when I am with someone[4]" his accent[5] was somewhere from the EU[6]. Mustard yellow[7] American[10] school bus[8] on a quiet[9] road[11] on a warm sunny day[12]. Driver[13] was thin with olive[14] skin[15] and wore a red[16] t-shirt[17]. He had straight black[18] hair[19] around his shoulders[20]. He was about to make a turn at a junction[21].

Below are the nouns and their meanings from my Dream Lexicon.

Male = a male part of me
Tick = emotionally tick
Day = periods that have the early part of life designated for emotional activity or the early stage of life and the dark part of life designated for emotional rest or the final stage of life
Someone = an emotional part of me (unknown)
Accent = manner of verbally communicating emotions

EU = emotional part that contains the wider emotional part of me made up of different emotional units

Mustard yellow = inclination toward depression and melancholy, lack of love and low self-worth

School bus = emotional vehicle on which other parts can move, on a bigger emotional vehicle that other parts of me use. It stops at the emotional learning environment for young parts of me travelling on a fixed emotional route

Quiet = Emotionally quiet

American = false substitute for the place I live in, my base and foundation

Road = emotional path for emotional vehicles

Warm Sunny Day = an emotionally pleasant and bright day

Driver = emotional part in charge of the direction of an emotional vehicle

Olive (colour) = resentment, greed and selfish desire

Skin = inner emotions

Red = energy, passion, love, lust, action, ambition, determination, anger and sexual passion

T-shirt = casual outer emotion

Black = hidden, secretive, unknown, mysterious, powerful, controlling, keeping emotions bottled up

Hair = emotions on top

Shoulders = upper part of the most emotionally flexible part attached to the most emotionally dexterous part that connects it with the emotional being

Junction = an emotional point where two or more set emotional routes, which lead to fixed emotional destinations are joined

The following is my analysis of this dream, which I will present in sections. The nouns have been substituted for other nouns within the square brackets, making it possible to see how the dream begins to reveal the emotional message from the subconscious. It is feasible to understand this further when the original description is removed.

Male voice said, "Do you know I tick once a day?"
Another male voice said, "I tick too".

A [male part of me] said, " do you know I [emotionally tick] once a [period which has the early part of life designated for emotional activity or the early stage of life and dark part of life designated for emotional rest or the final stage of life]?" another [a male part of me] said, " I [emotionally tick] too".

Analysis: This part of the dream means that an emotional male part of my subconscious is telling another emotional male part that they will be in harmony with each other later on in my life.

"Once when I am with someone." His accent was somewhere from the EU.

"Once when I am with [an emotional part of me (unknown)]" [his manner of verbally communicating emotions] was somewhere from [the emotional part that contains the wider emotional part of me, made up of different emotional units].

Analysis: Once this male part of me is with another part of me, it understands the broader emotional language made up of different emotional units.

254

Mustard yellow US school bus on a quiet road on a warm sunny day.

[Emotional vehicle that other parts can move on a bigger emotional vehicle that other parts of me use, and it stops at emotional learning environment for young parts of me travelling on a fixed emotional route] from [false substitute for the place that I live in, my base and foundation] of [inclination toward depression and melancholy, lack of love and low self-worth on a quiet [emotional path for emotional vehicles] on an [emotionally pleasant and bright day].

Analysis: The young emotional parts of me were taken to an emotional learning environment to learn to be depressed and melancholic, with a lack of love, where they also learned to have low self-worth even though the emotional environment appeared pleasant and bright. Their route to this place was emotionally quiet and bright, contrasting with their final destination.

Driver was thin, with olive skin and wore a red t-shirt.

[Part in charge of the direction of an emotional vehicle] was [emotionally thin] with [inner emotions] of [resentment, greed and selfish desire] and wore a [casual outer emotion] of [energy, passion, love, lust, action, ambition, determination, anger and sexual passion].

Analysis: The part that was in control of the destination of the young parts of me, on the surface, had good intentions, but underneath had bad intentions. Here I contrast the colour of the clothes with the colour of the driver's skin. *He had straight black hair around his shoulders.*

He had straight [emotions on top] of [hidden, secretive, unknown, mysterious, powerful, controlling, keeping emotions bottled up] around his [upper part of the most emotionally flexible part that is attached to the most emotionally dexterous part that connects it with the emotional being].

Analysis: This man does not want to reveal his true intentions because he has black hair. There are parts of the dream that I do not consider relevant in the analysis. It is helpful to keep the complete description when analysing dreams to understand the context fully.

For example, the emotional description of 'shoulders' does not add to the message, but *He was about to make a turn at a junction.*

He was about to make a turn at an [emotional point where two or more set emotional routes which lead to fixed emotional destinations are joined].

Analysis: This man is at a point where he controls the direction and destinations of the younger emotional parts of me before deciding upon the destination. Since his hair is black, the younger parts of me do not know where they will end up.

This dream is an example of how my subconscious began revealing problems in my childhood, and subsequent dreams have explored the issues in greater depth.

Dream Analysis and Automatic Writing

Dream Analysis takes time and effort, but it is an effective exercise. I found that if done regularly and accurately, my tinnitus dramatically reduced soon after. Later on, in my practice, I used the method of Automatic Writing to inform myself of what the dream meant rather than analysing this consciously, which proved faster and more effective. This happened when I was consciously familiar with most of the definitions and could recognise them. I defined a subconscious part of me called My Dream Analysing Friend. The label helped this part to come to work when it was time to analyse dreams. Although this may sound childish, it was vital to define this part as helpful and for a specific purpose to signal my subconscious to use this part in analysing dreams.

As seen below, I start by writing an invitation to My Dream Analysing Friend. Using Clean Language (see p. 179), I ask it what dreams and hypnagogia mean.

Hello, My Dream Analysing Friend; once again, please could you tell me, using your extraordinary wisdom, what these dreams and hypnagogia mean and what they teach me. Is there a feeling?

Okay, my friend, the dream analysis part of me, your wisdom will be appreciated. Please could you tell me what these dreams teach me? Is there a feeling?

Hi there, My Dream Analysing Friend, once again, what do these dreams and hypnagogia mean, and what do I need to learn from them? Is there a feeling?

The three examples above have been taken from three days of analysing dreams, where the content is the same, but the words are different. This is because I wanted to avoid developing the habit of using the same language each time. After all, habits dull the reaction from the subconscious and are more associated with the conscious.

I write my dreams down immediately after having them, and when I am ready to begin analysing them, I read all the dreams one after the other. I write an invitation to My Dream Analysing Friend in a separate document, then I create a small window where it is possible to see one dream at a time, and I read this dream and begin Automatic Writing. My subconscious indicates when it has finished analysing one dream and wants to move on to the next because the Automatic Writing says, 'and in the next dream of today...'. This ensures that the subconscious can completely express what it wants about a dream. This tells me I need to read the following dream and again write automatically. Even though Automatic Writing is not as detailed, I repeat this process until all the dreams have been analysed using Automatic Writing. This is because the insights are often deeper when analysing dreams subconsciously, and the information is sufficient to understand the emotional messages the dream contains. Having analysed dreams manually, I am already familiar with the vocabulary in the lexicon.

Using Metaphors From Dreams In Wakefulness

It is possible to create customised contexts using words that the subconscious has already associated with metaphors; in my case, these metaphors are recognisable elements of dreams. "Linguistic cues may bias our offline simulations in a similar way to how they bias perception, bringing particular content to awareness."[170] Sometimes simply thinking of the metaphor and its meaning when I undertook a particular action would be enough to experience silence. In this chapter, I have outlined how dreams reveal what I need to realise consciously. Dream Analysis provides insights into internal conflict through subconscious messages to help gain understanding and perspective. I discuss how dream metaphors are used daily to reduce tinnitus. I developed this method using the notion that dream metaphors would eventually become a common language between the subconscious and the conscious and could also be used by the conscious while awake.

Those who write about hypnosis refer to this practice as 'waking hypnosis', which is about using hypnosis mindfully to create a therapeutic experience in daily life. Here is one example of how a metaphor was used to reduce tinnitus. I was eating a mango one day while having loud tinnitus. A mango is defined as a light yellow fruit. According to my Dream Lexicon, a fruit is a 'natural raw, nutritious emotional nourishment as a result of emotional labour', and the colour yellow means to 'help to clear the mind, making it open and alert'. As I ate this fruit, I simultaneously thought of this metaphorical definition. As I engaged with the combination of the experience of eating the fruit while thinking about the associated metaphor, the tinnitus went down straight away. This is one example of the benefits of using metaphors therapeutically in a waking state. At other times, it was inappropriate to engage the subconscious like this since this would have meant that the tinnitus would have become louder.

An example of this is when I wear a black jumper. The definition of a jumper in my lexicon is 'warm outer emotions', while the colour black is defined as 'hidden, secretive, unknown, mysterious, powerful, controlling, keeping emotions bottled up'. Therefore, the definition of a black jumper is 'warm outer emotions' of 'hidden, secretive, unknown, mysterious, powerful, controlling, keeping emotions bottled up'. This kind of metaphor could have been harmful if I had brought it to my conscious awareness; it may have resulted in the tinnitus becoming louder. I need to consider when this exercise is beneficial and less so in other circumstances. Hence, this is the reason that I am mindful of engaging with this exercise.

Emotional Residue

The emotional residue is the tinnitus that I heard after a powerful and vivid dream or after completing an Automatic Writing session where the tinnitus was loud. This residue should not be confused with tinnitus, even though it often sounds the same. The emotional residue is the noise that does not have emotions attached; it is what is left behind, like the tracks in the sky after a plane has gone by. Essentially, these tracks consist of nothing but fade with time. In my work with dreams, I have learnt to recognise the distinction between tinnitus and emotional residue, even though this can sometimes be subtle. The residue is what is heard before the tinnitus disappears, especially when the revelation is large and significant. Although this process can take a few minutes to a couple of hours, experiencing this is incredibly comforting and reassuring.

The Purpose Of Dreams After Tinnitus

Dreams help the subconscious to stay open to a wide range of emotional possibilities, which would stop the subconscious from collapsing as with a cave-in. My subconscious explores emotional extremes through dreams, which is why tinnitus does not return after recovery. Having emotionally charged dreams prevents emotional build-up in the subconscious, which may give rise to tinnitus again. The following dream is one example where I experienced extreme fear during the dream and shortly after waking up. The dream below is not about the metaphorical cave-in but explores the emotions of fear and hopelessness.

Dream: *I was in a mine that was about to cave in. I panicked as I was about to get out. I was unable to get out, and then the cave-in happened, and I was stuck. I knew I wouldn't be alive to see another day.*

Keeping the channel between the subconscious and the conscious open is necessary. Emotional extremes help the subconscious to stay receptive to all possibilities. The subconscious explores extremes, making the tinnitus loud for a short while, but the noise that is heard is only emotional residue.

Dreams are a window into the subconscious and a detailed insight into what the subconscious wishes to express if analysed with care. Dream Analysis can often dramatically lower tinnitus. If Dream Analysis is done correctly and persistently, we can better know ourselves by revealing our emotional history and subconscious desires. This provides us with a better emotional insight into ourselves than those who do not have a method of accessing the subconscious.

Part E - Exercises

I often found my tinnitus was loud, and I needed a way of bringing the sound down when Automatic Writing did not work, or I was not in a position to write, for example, when I was out and did not have a pen and paper at hand. The mental exercises on the following pages gave me another method to draw upon when needed. I hope some of these exercises will work for the reader as well.

Chapter 16

Exercises for the Subconscious

Max Jones, a Teaching Associate at the University of Bristol, UK, who lectures in philosophy of psychology, philosophy of mind, and Sam Wilkinson, a Lecturer at the University of Exeter, UK, are of the view that the "Imagination is often *voluntary* and *goal-directed*, and must therefore be *constrained*."[171] This demonstrates that hypnosis makes it possible to direct the imagination to elicit positive change. The imagination is not the free association of ideas but has goal-directed activities which we need to maintain control over.

This chapter examines how the subconscious can be encouraged to reveal itself through various mental exercises one can complete in one's own time to help reduce or eliminate tinnitus. The more tools I have in my toolbox, the greater the variety of problems I can solve since I know how to use these when I need to; this is also true for treating tinnitus. It became essential for me to have various hypnosis exercises that I could choose from when the tinnitus was loud. Most of the exercises outlined in this chapter are from my amazing hypnotherapy sessions, where David taught me about them. I have also included some exercises that I thought of independently of David. I have tried these exercises more than a dozen times with positive results. These exercises can be done anytime and anywhere, reminding us that hypnosis is a way of being, a way of life and a way of remaining connected to the subconscious.

Relearning To Feel

When I first had tinnitus and was in a situation where the appropriate response was, for example, to feel anger, this emotion would express itself consciously as frustration. When I ought to have felt frustration, I felt sad. This meant that the entire emotion of anger or frustration was not felt at the conscious level, but it expressed itself in a diluted form, and the remainder stayed in the subconscious. Frustration is a diluted form of anger, while sadness is a diluted form of frustration. This was one of the reasons that my tinnitus became louder at times. Once I understood this through David, it was possible to be mindful to ensure that the entire emotion came up to the conscious. The exercise below solved this, and I instantly learned to feel the appropriate and complete emotion.

Snail Mail to Email

We all know what different emotions mean and how to describe them. Even though I knew what emotions meant, I had lost the ability to feel them, so it was important to relearn this ability again.

Imagine emotions from the past come by snail mail, but emotions should arrive instantly, like email. The conscious must learn to process emotions as soon as they need to be felt because email is a way of communicating instantly. Having no time delay between incoming

264

emotions and feelings and processing those emotions is paramount. The way I taught myself to do this was to set up an email account that I would never look at. As soon as I thought I was supposed to have a negative reaction to what I experienced at the moment, I would write this in an email while guessing how I would react emotionally if I had the ability. Then, I sent this email away, symbolising getting rid of the emotion from my system. I was pleasantly surprised when the tinnitus dramatically reduced its volume, which meant that what I had guessed as the correct reaction was accurate. Within a few months, I had taught myself to respond appropriately to emotional stimuli without the need to write them down. This was a small but crucial step towards full recovery.

The example below is something that I wrote after my tinnitus became loud, and I sent it to the email account I never opened. What should be noticed here is that not only did I describe the incident straight after my tinnitus became louder, but also how I imagined I would have felt if I could feel at the time. For example, I used words like "anxious" when describing my feelings and "stress" and "anger" when describing the feelings of my friend. It was vital that I did this straight after my tinnitus became loud because I could identify the incident immediately. Had this writing been undertaken later, it would have been difficult to pinpoint the particular incident from so many throughout the day.

> *"My friend was stressed on Saturday morning. My carer was late and my friend who had stayed the night to look after me had to go to work. She sounded really angry on the phone as she barked instructions to people about what to do while arguing with them. I felt really anxious about it all. I don't know why, it wasn't my fault. I felt out of*

control and could feel her anger, even though it was not directed at me. When my carer arrived, she apologised but she had so much trouble with the trains because of the delay at the station. I really was relieved to see her as my friend ran out of the door."

In the initial stages of my recovery, by describing the events and associated emotions in words, I learned to feel emotions for the first time after many years of being unable to do this. This was also one way that the tinnitus went down immediately. It was helpful when I took some time to think about how I should have felt. If you attempted this exercise, I recommend carefully considering the emotions you are writing about.

Conscious Understanding Of Emotions

In the Introduction, I describe the importance of taking the journey from the land of knowing to the land of realising, stressing that we need to engage emotionally to realise. The exercise below was done in the initial stages of my treatment. I put descriptions of emotions into general categories that I thought were appropriate to how I felt about myself then. This exercise was helpful since it helped me begin re-engaging with how I perceived myself at an emotional level, which was the crucial first step to feeling any emotions at all. The examples below are from my initial work, and their meaning is so personal to me that they will not apply to anyone else, but I have included them to demonstrate the exercise.

Disconnected Brain and Body

Unsupported, Does not fit, Accepted, Unworthy, Notice, Free, Weird, Connect, Disconnected, Burden, Imposing, Standing up for myself, Horrible, Friend, Do not fit, Rebel, Never chosen, Booby prize, Strength, Oddball, Embarrassment, Patronised

Rebel, cowboy and an Outlaw

Dependent, Bold, Insightful, Determined, Ambitious, Childlike, Free spirited, Ambitious, Compassionate, Revolutionary, Burdened, Childlike freedom, Closed, Unattractive, Fair, Overlooked, Separated, Scruffy mind, Confident, Not cute or lovable, Misunderstood, Discomfort, Courage

Weird When I Have Positive Attention

Friendly, Craziness, Invisible, Integrity, Weak, Invisible, Imposing, Bold, Dependent, Ignored, Useless, Free, Respectful of other people, Mean, Untrusting, Closed, Ignored, Unconsidered, Disbelieving, Nonconformist, Physically unworthy, Undervalued, Alone, Cynical

Important to Someone

Valued, Confident, Freedom, Unequal, Useful, Spontaneity, Bondage, Clumsy manner, Reliable, Understanding, Restricted, Looked down upon, Alien, Misunderstood, Relaxed, Unconfident, Tiny, Unimportant, Unimposing, Low self-esteem, Odd, Frustration, Vulnerable

Low Self-Perception

Booby prize, Chicken, Cowboy, Independence, Kid at heart, Free-spirited, Reliable, Dependable, Independent, Free-thinking, Low self-confidence, Injustice, Peace-loving, Challenging, Outlaw, Considerate, Bold, Unflinching, Mental limitations, Upset, Positive, Satisfaction

I took each word and wrote about what it meant and how it applied to me while giving an example from my life. This exercise appears to be meant for primary school children, but it is worth remembering that consciously forgotten emotions need to be retrieved with ease and care. After this, it seemed to have put the emotions back into the conscious because I could summon the correct emotion in response to any situation. This reduced the tinnitus, and once the emotions had been relearned by the conscious, they remained there. In the example below, I have written about the feeling of being frustrated, and I described times when I felt this feeling. This is how the conscious could relearn this feeling, and once it was reinstated into the conscious, it was possible for this feeling to come up consciously at the appropriate time.

Frustrated

"I'm so frustrated with my tinnitus because it is not going down or away and I'm not sure what to do any more. My psychotherapist is not working and it will be another month until I see her again. I know the tinnitus is capable of disappearing because it has done for one week at a time. I don't think I have the energy to get angry enough to kick it out but I really want to. If the tinnitus can go down before, then it can go again but I need the energy to kick it out with my anger. Spending one day with my nephew and the other animals did not help Mister Angry

Man at all so I think I need another idea for the emotions to come but don't know what. I wish my friend was here. I'm so frustrated with it all. I am so frustrated that I couldn't take my nephew out today like I said I would. We were meant to go to Battersea to see the animals, but I had such a terrible migraine last night. I'm so frustrated that I couldn't keep my word to him and now he is bored which makes me even more frustrated. I'm so fed up and frustrated about how tinnitus takes over my life and gets me to dance to its tune, well no more, enough is enough I am taking my life back with the help of mister angry man. I am so frustrated with the whole damn system of treatment for tinnitus and if someone had told me earlier what to do and in fact there was a way out and told me what I needed to do rather than me finding out for myself then things would have been a lot easier and I wouldn't have suffered so much and thought I was going mad. I am so frustrated with it all that I feel like saying to blazes with the NHS and how dare they ruin my life and give me a life sentence when there had always been alternatives to treating tinnitus and I am so very frustrated that I had to learn this on my own over a long period of time in which time I had gone mad already but no one saw it except David and my friend and psychotherapist. I feel so frustrated that I sometimes want to hit my head against a wall to make the sound go away, it is invisible to other people and they don't see anything of what I go through. When I should be spending time with my nephew or doing my uni work I am writing instead just to get a bit of peace and quiet."

I wrote about several other emotions in the same way, providing examples of when I should have felt a particular emotion. This is how it became possible to reintroduce these emotions into the conscious, where they became available at the correct times.

Emotions And The Colour Spectrum

In the Analysing Dreams chapter, we have seen how different colours are associated with different emotions. This provides some language to understand dreams and what they say about the emotions within the subconscious. When we have become familiar with the emotional associations of the different colours of the spectrum, it is helpful to do the following exercise to have a conscious understanding of the variety of emotions available and how one emotion changes into another.

The subconscious and the conscious need access to all the emotions at all times to use the right emotions at the right time. This playful exercise taught me how colours are combined to make new colours; colours represent emotions in the Dream Lexicon (see p. 248). I imagine a range of shades in this exercise, for example, from white to navy and black. So, I imagine how white gradually turns into navy and how navy gradually turns into black. By imagining all the colour ranges of blue, I can also do this backwards from black to navy and subsequently to white. I did this with all the primary colours over a couple of days. This is to help the subconscious learn how to recombine colours to make new ones, i.e., learn to recombine several emotions to create emotional variety. For example, I also imagine light clear yellow, which, in my Dream Lexicon, helps to clear the mind, making it open and alert. In contrast, dark yellow is an inclination toward depression, melancholy, lack of love and low self-worth. These opposite emotions are, in fact, on the same spectrum but at either end, and this exercise makes it possible to see the journey of how one emotion at one end of the spectrum turns into another at the opposite end. By consciously moving through the colour range, this reminds the subconscious that it has a variety of emotions that are also available to the conscious and that it can identify and move through them without barriers. This reminds the conscious that there is another way of communicating apart from tinnitus and that the subconscious and the conscious now have a common language. My tinnitus went down by half when I did this the first time. I also imagine, for example, putting a small quantity of white in dark yellow to make it light clear yellow. In reverse, when a small amount of black is added to light clear yellow, it becomes dark yellow. I invite the reader to be creative and experiment with the colour ranges. By exploring the spectrum of colours and associating each colour with emotion, this exercise helps the conscious re-engage with various emotions that were out of bounds to the conscious.

Repairing The Past Exercises

"Rossi: So this is a basic process of hypnotherapy: *reperceiving emotional processes as the essence of reframing them.*

Erickson: You don't alter the original experience; you alter the perception of it, and that becomes the memory of the perception."[172]

The quote above inspired me to develop the Cycle of Silence Exercise, which I used to remedy the emotional trauma of my past. This exercise aims to alter the emotional perception of my memory by weakening the emotional trauma but without distorting the emotional reality. It is crucial not to contort emotional reality because this can lead to 'happy fantasies', which can lead to denial, and of course, the denial of trauma is one cause of tinnitus. There is a fine line between changing the emotional impact of trauma by diluting it and distorting emotional reality, so what we imagine is not what happened. This is not a good idea since this will lead to the denial of trauma. These exercises are based on creating the cycle of repair between David, the child me, and me at present so that a positive feedback loop reverses the repudiation of trauma by the conscious. It is possible to do this exercise by imagining someone like a close friend or anyone else you trust and feel safe with, which in my case, could be David or Phil.

The Cycle Of Silence

The emotional direction that I was forced to take as a child resulted in my subconscious becoming less able to communicate with the conscious. The following exercises are designed for me to go back in time emotionally to a point before the trauma and take another emotional route. While the events of my life remain the same, how I respond to them has changed. Consequently, my emotions remain open while my conscious maintains contact with my subconscious. In this exercise, I invite the subconscious to go back to a "safe" emotional time in my childhood and make a connection between me in the past and myself in the present. Providing one experience is created by the imagination and the memory within the subconscious; I bring up the memory of silence before I had tinnitus to experience it in the present while delivering comfort and the experience of hypnosis to the younger version of myself. Silence is invited to travel down a safe and strong tube connecting me in the present to me as a child. A wormhole is a hypothetical topological feature that would be a shortcut, connecting two separate points in the spatiotemporal dimension, where it becomes possible to connect experiences regardless of how far apart in time they are. In this exercise, I use this metaphor to access a moment in my past where I had experienced trauma. I imagined David to be my emotional guide to recovering from tinnitus.

Since hypnosis has no boundaries to what is possible, in this exercise, I give the young me the experience of being with David, as if she had hypnotherapy sessions with him. In return, she gives the present me the memory of silence. The past becomes the present for a short while. By presenting the experience of David to the younger version of myself, the lived emotional experience of my past is unaltered. What changes is the coping mechanism of how I dealt with past trauma. This is important because changing the memory of what happened could be seen as denying the past. In this exercise, I give the younger version of myself the ability to cope emotionally with what I experienced as a child. It is a fair swap where both of us have emotional recovery simultaneously.

The following is a three-part exercise, and each part can be done independently, but if done together, they must be in the following order.

Roots Of Silence - Part One

The roots of a tree can be thought of as my emotional roots, which have been formed in the past and from which I have grown into the present like a tree. Roots are underground and not visible, but they bring up nutrients to help the tree grow. If the roots are damaged or in contaminated soil, this makes for an unhealthy tree. Similarly, my past did not provide the emotional nourishment that I needed. this exercise can repair my past emotionally while providing the nourishment I need.

My left ear had tinnitus, but the right did not. In this exercise, I imagine two trees, one at each ear where the tinnitus is. The tinnitus at the left ear has made the tree lose its leaves, and it is bare and black, while the other tree at the right ear appears like a beautiful tree between spring and summer. I now imagine I am an excellent gardener, and I carefully cut a main branch of the summer tree. I listen to my tinnitus while identifying the exact place of the sound and imagine that the black and unhealthy tree is superimposed onto the area of the sound. Then I identify the location of the sound on the tree, making an incision in the bare and black tree where the tinnitus is located, and carefully graft the other tree's healthy branch into this space.

I imagine the graft of the silent healthy tree growing into the black tree, giving it life. I visualise this with my body, where my feet are the roots, and my head and arms are branches. Then slowly, I imagine the graft of the silent tree growing into me. It forms roots which combine with my black tinnitus roots. The graft eventually takes over the whole of the other tree, resurrecting the black tree.

This exercise does not always work straight away. I need to keep imagining this every few minutes after putting the initial graft into the black tree; this exercise requires patience for it to succeed. This could be because, even though it is quite a gentle exercise, it is also quite robust. After all, trees grow gradually and strongly over a long time. In my experience, this is good for when the tinnitus does not go down by other methods.

The Whispering Exercise – Part Two

We might get stuck into a vicious cycle of thinking determined by the experience in our past, which is unhelpful in moving forward emotionally. Gilligan suggests a remedy,

> Another way to open multiple possibilities is called
> the *generating new choices method.* It operates

on our core premise that when we get stuck, we can use trance to (1) release the negative pattern, (2) connect deeply with the quantum deep structure of the pattern, which holds many possible forms, and (3) then generate new forms that will more positively express the need or intention of the deeper core.[173]

My trauma left me stuck in certain patterns of thinking where I could not explore ways to recover. The Whispering Exercise came to my mind when I considered moments in my past that were particularly painful. I needed a way to navigate the pain without blocking out the memory. Gilligan has a term for the times in our past when we were neglected, denied or repressed, whether by ourselves or by other people. He calls this our neglected Self. This is a physiological feeling of being fixed or frozen in time,[174] and though I had this feeling for most of my life, it intensified just before the onset of tinnitus. Gilligan explains that, "Touching the center activates the proper experiential reference. Until this happens, the idea of a neglected self seems like psychobabble."[175]

Often when I visited David, he encouraged me in the present to connect with me in the past. However, this process is also possible without a therapist. The conscious assumes the role of a therapist by guiding and not interfering with the subconscious process. The following exercise is when I bring emotional recovery to the times in my past when I felt neglected and when I needed David the most. The cognitive Self (affecting cognitive ability) and the somatic Self (involved in the mind/body relationship) are both present and responsive at the same time. The aim is to develop experience within a relational context between the two Selves. Joel Pearson, who has a research interest in

Mental imagery, Consciousness, Intuition, Visual Working Memory, Science of Innovation, said that, "The neural representation of mental imagery has been shown to be very similar to that of actual perception, even in relatively low-level areas of the visual cortex..."[176] The Whispering Exercise works by neutralising my negative emotions and experience of a time of emotional distress by altering my emotional response to it. I practise another version of this exercise when I feel alone and neglected. I imagine holding Phil's hand, which brings up feelings of comfort and love from the subconscious to the conscious, and where I need his presence. This is particularly beneficial in moments when I need the courage to face whatever challenge there is before me.

Exercise

I imagine myself as a young girl in a certain environment; this could be an actual memory or something from my imagination. David is in the distance, walking towards me, and as he comes nearer, I become more joyful. I notice what I wear and make this vivid. When David is by me, we smile at each other. He indicates for me to look straight ahead while he comes to my left and, bending down, whispers in my ear. I do not consciously know what he says, but my subconscious does.

Spending a few years with David has given me some of his wonderful knowledge of hypnosis. This exercise aims to evoke this knowledge in the younger version of myself, providing her with the coping mechanisms to deal with whatever she experiences in my childhood. It is possible to do this exercise by imagining anyone else that you know, but you should ensure that you trust their wisdom.

Finding Another Way – Part Three

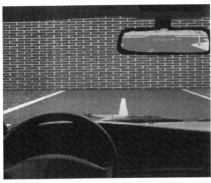

In this exercise, I imagine that I am driving a car. I see that I have driven down a road, and I see a brick wall in front of me. I take some time to acknowledge that I am at a dead end and gently remind my subconscious that it needs to reverse the car onto the main road. I ask my subconscious to consider the empty road behind me, asserting that there are many roundabouts. I am the driver in the only car here because all these roads behind me belong to me.

I gently remind my subconscious of these two facts while encouraging it to slowly reverse the car away from the brick wall into the road. At this point, the tinnitus usually goes down, and I can either stop the exercise here or continue with the Roads and Roundabouts exercise (see p. 173) while writing automatically.

When these three exercises are combined in this order, in my experience, this makes for a powerful exercise in itself and often reduces tinnitus considerably. The Roots of Silence is a foundation exercise where the subconscious is encouraged to generate silence by transferring silence from one ear to the other ear but at a deep emotional level, like the roots of a tree. This leads to the whispering and memory of silence exercise, where the experience of David whispering into the ear of the young me provides the young me with the experience and wisdom of David. So in this way, the young me is like the tree's roots, and this experience is like repairing the tree's roots by giving David's wisdom to the younger version of myself from the past. This wisdom is free to affect me positively in the future, which is my present.

When the young version of myself gets the wisdom of David, she whispers the experience of silence into the ear of the present me. This is how the memory of silence comes up from the past to the present. This leads to the exercise of the car being encouraged to reverse away from the brick wall, which is important because the nature of tinnitus means that trapped emotions within the subconscious cannot escape.

The metaphor of the car going into reverse reminds the subconscious that emotions can back away from an emotional barrier. It takes another route that is full of freedom of expression, like the empty roads and the Roads and Roundabouts (a process of Automatic Writing). When the car reverses away from the wall, it is as if the younger version of myself (in the second exercise) has an alternative emotional future because she has the wisdom of David, which is, in effect, me in the present. This is a possible explanation of how this exercise works for me to reduce tinnitus and the relationship between the three exercises. This process may repair the emotional path that connects the past me, the younger me, to myself in the present.

Chapter 17

Burning Letters

There were some emotions that were stuck inside me. They were associated with two traumatic events in my past, and there was no easy way to get rid of them because they were too big, deep-rooted and complicated. They were like the roots of a dead tree, entangled with the roots of a living one.

I had done all that I could with hypnosis, but my dreams suggested that there was still work to be done. The first trauma was the trauma of being born with a disability, knowing that the negligence of the medical staff of the hospital caused this. The second was all about my experience at the special needs school. It was impossible to go back and confront the people responsible for my traumas or how I was treated because the staff in the hospital had moved on or retired, and my school had closed many years ago. However, I knew my subconscious had not completely processed these emotions because they reoccurred in my dreams. David suggested that my subconscious needed closure in any case, and that I should write a letter to these institutions without holding anything back, expressing my anger at them over what they had done to me and how their actions had affected my life. I decided to write these letters using Automatic Writing (punctuation has been added to make them easier to read) since I trusted my subconscious to express all it needed.

David and I spent several sessions doing the groundwork for my subconscious for the necessary closure. The issues were so foundational to my tinnitus that they needed special care and extra attention to ensure that my subconscious had processed all the associated emotions.

After I wrote these letters, David read them, and by signing them, he acknowledged that he was a witness. He instructed me to burn the letters and scatter the ashes somewhere. As I cannot use my hands, I asked my nephew to help me burn the letters. Having him there was comforting, and it made the occasion joyful. I wrote a poem for each of the ceremonies where I said goodbye to that particular event (see below), which my nephew read out. The result was amazing; these issues stopped featuring in my dreams altogether, indicating that I had the closure I desperately needed. The Epilogue on p. 330 describes a similar ceremony with my friend Phil, where I finally said goodbye to the past to acknowledge my full recovery from tinnitus.

Letter to Hospital

Maternity Unit

19.01.2013

My birth and the time I was born

Dear Doctors of the idiot zone,

I'm writing to you about when I was born. You cut out my life with a sharp knife by depriving me of oxygen.

Why didn't you turn me again and again when I was in my mum's tummy? That would have solved everything, it is as simple as that, but you didn't do that, did you?

When the time was right, I had to fight for breath and I died when I should have lived so my brain was deprived of oxygen.

I have Cerebral Palsy now because of your negligence but I can't do anything about it, anything at all. Which is why I never stand tall but always remain small, in your eyes at least.

What a beast you were, what a beast you are, you told my mum I will never understand, I will never recognise my own name or turn my head to look at her when she calls my name because they would all be the same to me, just noises in my head.

When one of your beloved nurses came around she had a doll in her hand to be raffled away to brighten some new mum's day. My mum bought those tickets and said she would buy all if you could guarantee that I would understand, one day, what she said, but you shook your head in dismay and walked away.

I was told by my mum that a junior doctor was there at the time of my birth, my mum didn't trust him at first. This dark haired junior doctor would impair my future for sure by never turning me once more.

So I came out of my mum, feet first, he cut the umbilical cord while I was thirsty for air. I was half inside my mum and half of me was out, I died because of this, without a doubt.

When my mum first laid eyes on the junior doctor, her instincts kicked in, she would never trust this man, he was dim. He was never properly trained in an understaffed hospital, he was no good from within.

They rushed me to the incubator that seemed miles away, with no time to waste and no time to see the light of day.

I didn't even say hi to my dad as I was whizzed by the hospital corridors and minutes later I was in an incubator. But it was too late, the damage had been done when my life had only just begun.

Congratulations, I survived but with you I nearly died. Cerebral Palsy is what I had, that was what you told my dad and my mum too.

Will she walk? Will she understand her own name? When I call her, will she turn her head and recognise her own name? My parents were eager to know and their questions simply flowed.

You told my mum and dad don't hope for much more, if she recognises you, she will be on the floor, she will be remarkable if she recognises you and turns her head to look at you.

But don't ask for much more, and don't expect for much more, because miracles is not what we do.

When I was two, they asked me what is two and two, I said four of course, didn't you know? Walking was impossible, sitting was impossible, if I was not held up I would fall down. My hands wouldn't listen to what I say, if I wanted them to go a certain way, they would go the other way.

My legs couldn't hold me up either because they were wobbly like jelly. And all together I was a mess because of your negligence and insanity. How am I to cope with that?

People patronising me and staring at me but that was that. You packed me home, one month after I was born and told me to go, get on with it, your life has gone. Don't look back here again because you should be grateful that we saved your life.

Actually, the damage you have done I will never overcome and no one could ever see the potential in me. I continued life as a special needs child but actually I died inside when I survived.

What you have done is down to your negligence and neglect, something that you are renowned for, something that you do best.

When I was eighteen, not a whisper, not a word from you to say you are sorry for what you had to do.

Life has been hard, living like a retard when I know so much and I want my life to be so rich. I went to a special school because of you and I broke all the rules because I could think for myself so I thought, this life is not for me, I can do better in an environment free of disability. But I was stuck there like fly-paper on the wall when I really wanted to grow tall. But I couldn't grow because the ceilings were too low so they squashed me inside and I nearly died.

When I went out in my wheelchair and met other people they would look at me and wonder if I can understand. "Hello, is anyone at home, dear?" But they were missing the point, they were never at home and they would never grow tall. But they didn't recognise that in themselves, they saw that in me, again and again they would ask is she happy with our company?

I hate Cerebral Palsy and the mental health issues that it brought, for I was an intelligent and disabled girl in an able-bodied world. Everyone thought they knew better than me and would put me under their thumb rather than giving me the right company.

I wanted to learn so much but I had brain damage because of you and I couldn't balance or go to the loo on my own.

One turn of the tummy would have been all it took but you couldn't do that because you didn't look at which way was up or which way was down so I died for a few seconds under your frown.

My brain damage cannot be repaired, I am impaired physically but I am not vulnerable or scared.

Now I have David on my side, to be my guide and help me survive when I could have died, many years ago when the pressure got too much and I closed down emotionally, I couldn't do very much.

The world and society had its way, I wouldn't see a new day because I had to do things their way and not mine. One turn of the tummy and my mum would have known I could recognise that doll one day instead of waiting for me to grow up and saying I will do things my way.

One turn of the tummy was all it took to prevent my disability and to remove me from hell in that brook, down in the valley, where nobody goes, I sit alone, looking down at my toes, thinking why me? Why me?

But no answer comes but I know it is because of your negligence and I know I will overcome. How tough is life now? I hear you ask, I am not under a veil and I am not under a mask. So, see for yourself how tough life is, you know what you have done and you know you cannot undo what you have done.

But I hear you say don't give in, I congratulate you, I'm proud of you. Yeah, and you expect me to say thank you for that remark, what you have done to me is to bark up the wrong tree.

I hate you for what you have done but I will overcome on my own and build myself a nice new home without you and your lot because I know what I am doing, I am on the spot.

I broke the rules of disability and don't need your pity. I'm a broken woman living in the real world because of what you have done but I will overcome, I will survive. As I sit here and write this letter to you, I wonder how many babies have died and how many have survived, how many lives have you destroyed in the process? It is all a mess and I regret being born on your ward.

Yours sincerely,

Sapna Ramnani, Doctor to be (because someone saw the potential in me)

This letter is witnessed by David Corr on 24th January 2013.

On a beautiful sunny day, my nephew burnt this letter in our back garden while I was with him. He is fond of baking, so we celebrated by  him making his wonderful cookies. There is a beautiful park near my house, and my nephew and I decided to scatter the ashes of the letter under an oak tree. He also read out the following poem that I wrote to mark the occasion.

20/01/2013

With eyes like thunder
I wonder how you could treat me this way?
Didn't you know I'm full of woe about beginning a new day?
In your hospital full of no hope
I couldn't cope
I wanted to tell you that tomorrow you will die if you told a lie
But you did because you thought I was dumb and I wouldn't overcome
One turn of the tummy was all it took
One turn of the tummy and I would have been okay
You said tomorrow you will die but you told a lie
You said tomorrow there is no hope and I wouldn't cope
Out there in a world which had nothing to give
My brain was like a broken sieve
Nothing went in and nothing went out
I couldn't prove to you that you were telling a lie
You said tomorrow I would die or end up as a vegetable on a shelf
somewhere
Looking into the abyss of nothingness
But I have David with his rainbows to pave the way for me

But you said tomorrow you will die

That is the future in a vegetable shop

In a special needs school getting the chop

One turn of the tummy was all it took

But you didn't care

You didn't look

Now David has to repair me again by making me new

Because I am through with you

Letter to School

I related the second traumatic experience to when I attended the special needs school. I also needed closure emotionally at this time in my life. Once again, I used Automatic Writing to give my subconscious a chance to express all the emotions associated with that horrible time. This is how I managed to let go of the past at the conscious and subconscious levels.

Dear Special Needs School,

I am sure you remember me because I am the girl who got away and who you thought would have no hope. I am now writing to you as a Ph.D. student, yeah that is right; a Ph.D. student and an Independent Documentary Film-maker because I am so angry with you and what you have done to me that I thought I would let you know.

When I was born I had Cerebral Palsy and I was put in your school and under your care because of this, but I may as well have gone to a Nazi concentration camp. You may think that I was treated well in my special needs school and by you and your staff, but I have tinnitus now, a noise in my ear twenty-four hours a day. I have come to learn that this noise is the noise of silent anger and frustration over my past.

How dare you and how could you have kept a girl like me under your care when you knew I was better than all that you have to offer me? How could you have destroyed my life and got away with it with no one to answer to?

I'm a Ph.D. student now and I make films, good films, informative films, so one could say I have made it despite it all, despite you and your long corridors with so many classrooms behind invisible iron bars. We were like chickens in a factory farm, cows waiting for the slaughterhouse. Should I really go on? I was like guinea fowl waiting for the bullet to hit me.

And people now pat me on the back and congratulate me for the life I am living and for the life I have designed for myself. It came at a price, my mental health, yeah I have mental health issues and I am a mental health survivor. But you always thought I was strong and could survive anything. Is this really the life I need to pay for surviving, escaping and returning to my own roots and destiny?

This is the destiny that I chose, but with silence without noise. It didn't happen because so much of my life has been taken away by you and I have only just found out. You murdered my spirit, you raped my mind, you put me in a straitjacket which nobody could see.

I had the potential, the seed of life to grow into something big, the woman I was meant to be without you and without it all. I became detached from you a long time ago before you ever ripped me apart which is why I stayed together and holding it all in, holding on for dear life. But I was lost when I didn't know I was lost and by the time I found out it was too late, I needed specialist help, I needed answers for why I was screaming so much inside, but why I became silent to all around me.

It was you and it began with you and no one else. For years, I hid this from myself, denying it all, burying it deep within me. A volcano came out of me one day and I thought I would burst with the pain of noise when I so adored silence. This noise is your legacy to me because of a broken life, a broken childhood, a childhood that never was and never could be in your arms.

I was broken inside, but I never knew it because I worked like crazy to repair the damage you have done and I thought I had got there when I passed my GCSEs, because I was off the conveyor belt to the slaughterhouse and off the meat shelves.

You broke me again because of the volcano that you created in me, the one that I didn't know about. I hate you and I hate what you have done to me because I died after you lived because I died because of you.

Why did you put a straitjacket on me when you knew I couldn't move anyway? I don't know. I hated that and I hated you because I knew my potential, but you were blind. You were blind because you took away the best part of my life when I should have been learning and finding out about the world and what I wanted to do, it was so simple like other kids have.

I don't know what to do now and how much I want to tell you, how much I am in pain for the little girl who knew so much of your work and your darkness, but I couldn't do anything. Not only do I have Cerebral Palsy, but I have a mental health issue and I suppose it is because I am intelligent enough to know what happened and to feel the pain of you. I could have died, but my brain decided to turn off and feel numbness, nothing at all, yes this is how I survived a life away from the slaughterhouse, a life of no hope and definitely no future.

What did you expect from me? Did you expect me to sit in a day centre somewhere and enjoy a Christmas party or a day out to the seaside to look at the sea and eat some rock? I could have brought some home for my family as a souvenir of my day out with my wonderful friends who actually are not my real friends because they are dead behind their eyes, other victims of you.

If I were to tell you about some of my friends that I have now and those that I have come to know. People like Brian, a strong human rights advocate, we closed down an organisation together. Jenny, a brilliant and brave human rights journalist. I can almost hear you say how the hell did I end up with her?

And then there is yet another hero of mine, David, gosh, do you know, don't you realise or understand? He is the one who repaired the damage you have done and I would have died without him.

I imagine myself walking down that damn big hallway every day, the very centre of you and I wonder how the hell did I end up there? And how the hell did I get bad mental health? You took away so much from me, you and your staff, your impersonal staff who thought they knew it all. But they knew nothing at all like you about me and who I was, my hopes and dreams for the future and where I came from and where I wanted to go.

When I told one of your beloved staff that I wanted to go to university and in order to do this, I must pass my GCSEs, he was silent and then he said yes well maybe or maybe not. Is that the answer to give to a young girl with so many ambitions, so many dreams? I think not. It is quite unethical and it turns my stomach.

I knew then what I know now that I was and am alone in this world of disability and special needs that you created around me. I am alone because I am the one, the only survivor of your system, the one who had to pay the price of a normal education and a normal life because normal is not in your dictionary.

So I died because of that, because of your negligence and stupidity.

I will become Doctor Ramnani probably next year, but my personal life has gone because I have to fight hard for where I am now and I didn't have enough fight for my personal life. So something was left by the wayside. I am half a person now because of you and I am trying to get whole again and trying to take back and reclaim what is mine. There is a lot that is mine and there is a lot that doesn't belong to me.

You know what you have given me and it was an abuse of a little girl who wanted to be who she was meant to be before you came along. In one of my reports it said that I had very good comprehension and I could recognise the time and knew about money. Actually, I was fifteen when this report was written and I wonder what the conversation was like about me. In another report it said I could read and write, but I didn't have many friends and I think I was fifteen again.

Well considering all my friends had died or had left, what did you expect?

We were left with a bunch of kids with learning disabilities and me, the oddball. How I hated you for this and for the years that I spent in your classroom being patronised by your questions to me like what was the capital of England?

My darling nephew knew that when he was four or five or even younger. What the hell were you asking me for when you knew I was nearly seventeen? So I broke inside because I knew I was in trouble like a person trapped in a room when they can see the flames of a fire at their only escape. I could see those flames coming for me but you couldn't and none of your dead-eyed students could which is why I was a pain in your neck.

The difficult one, the one that was always different, but you couldn't put your finger on why or how.

I am now more qualified than you and all those you employed to look after me, but I am not proud of it because I know the truth of my potential and the truth of where I came from, it certainly doesn't have

293

anything to do with you.

And as I return to my roots, my original roots, I will bypass you because you were not my original and never made me whole. I return alone back home to where I came from in order to grow again without your sweet nectar poison and your charming manner that could have fooled anyone, but not me.

I return home again to grow again into the woman I was meant to be before you. The woman definitely with a disability, but without all that madness of suppression that made me dead inside.

I want to make human rights documentaries and in order to do this I am required to be sensitive to other people and their emotions. This is my passion and I know somewhere deep down I do this because I didn't have this from you.

Now special needs school I look you in the eyes as I look down at you for I am bigger than you and even though I am a hippy I kill you from my system, from my very being because you have destroyed my life enough and I have to return to my roots in order to grow my way and not yours.

If I see you again I know I will be in hell, but I actually don't believe in heaven or hell. If I hear your voice again I know I will be dead, but I am a survivor and will never die when I don't want to.

I'm a mental health survivor and a special needs survivor. I'm a-special needs school survivor, but to survive is not good enough for me, so I don't want you in my system anymore because I'm stronger than you and I have David, while you have nothing at all and nothing on me.

Sapna

01.01.2013: As I Scatter Your Ashes

As I scatter your ashes by your grave

I know what you have done and how you misbehaved

You took away my joy you stole it in the night

I had no choice but to go back and fight

I was lost and now I'm found

To my own destiny I am bound

I return to you all that is yours and in doing so I finally open the door

As I step out into the sunlight I will be in no darkness under your

shadow

For you are gone now

Never to come back

All I do now is go and pack for a new life

Now is where I belong

And I'll put right all that you've done wrong

The future is bright now as bright as day

Now that you have gone now

I have blown you away I step into my future now and what do I see?

A life without your shadow

Tall and looming over my destiny

In the forest of my destiny where you have cut down my trees

I will now nurture the earth

Nurture the land beneath me

Trees will grow around and they will not bend to your will

But they will grow strong

Straight and very still

Like the quietness of my mind and the silence I will find

A life now without you always overshadowing my mind

You have gone now and I will overcome

The pain

The loss

And the grief that you have done

When I return to the path that I was meant to follow

I will sing and fly like a beautiful swallow

My song will be of freedom

Not the loss of you

For as for me now

I'm quite sure I'm through

As I close the door to you I lock it very tight

You will no longer haunt my dreams as I sleep at night

You have gone from my mind

No more will you haunt my spirit

No more will you be unkind

For tomorrow is a new day without you and a new beginning too

I have kicked you out without a doubt and in doing so I will shout

"For you are gone now, you will haunt me no more"

To you I will slam the door

So don't come knocking for I won't be in

Not for you a gaunt little man ever so thin

Your power has gone now from within

Burnt into ash now as I grin

Those ashes were scattered at your door

But when I looked for you

You were on the floor

Lying there in a pool of blood

Before which I heard a thud

The giant has crashed now

Fallen down to the ground

Where he can do no wrong now to all around

He has gone

Gone from my system

My being

The very fibre of me

And in doing so I return to my destiny

Tomorrow will bring new joys and a new beginning

And without you I will always be winning

As I sit here now free as a bird I hear no whisper

No sound to be heard

In doing so your freedom is lost because as from now I'm the boss

I rule over my destiny like a bird in flight

Only resting for me will be done at night

I have dreams to follow and places to go

Mountains to climb and rivers to flow

The future is an adventure something far away

I will live to fight another day

Up through the mountains

Down to the sea I now fly high

Happy and free

With the freedom to roam

I now choose my own home

Chapter 18

Metaphor Exercises

This chapter explains the importance of being mindful in everything you do, ensuring that the subconscious is encouraged to stay open as you carry on with daily life, which can reduce tinnitus. Metaphors like fly-tipping allow this to happen through simple stories. I have used all of the exercises described in this and the following chapter daily, as David taught me over the years. In addition, I have used extracts from my journal to explain the effects. These exercises need to be used at one's discretion, and even though they have worked for me, they may not necessarily work for everyone.

Parts of the Body Exercises

Bladder Exercise

As I mentioned, one can do hypnosis anytime and anywhere, even on the loo. This exercise is based on a metaphor, and its meaning often came up in my dreams, where I got this idea. In Dream Lexicon, I expel negative toxic emotions when I dream of going to the loo. When I need to use the loo, I imagine the tinnitus is a red cluster made into a ball.

This way, I turn the tinnitus into something I visualise as tangible. I imagine the ball is fragmented, and these fragments move down into my bladder. I sit on the loo and continue to imagine the red fragments at the bottom of my bladder. I open my bladder for a short while (between 2 and 4 seconds) and stop the flow voluntarily by closing the bladder. Then, I imagine another few fragments of tinnitus going down into my bladder and repeating the exercise; the tinnitus often goes down pretty fast. For example, one day, when the tinnitus was at 4, it did not go down by any other method, but it went down to 1 when I did this exercise. In my experience, it is hard to do this exercise when I am desperate to go to the loo, so when I need to do this exercise, I make sure I go just before the feeling becomes urgent.

Controlling Tinnitus Exercise

One day, I intended to study but could not, as my tinnitus was at 4, driving me mad. When I did this exercise, it went down to 1 within thirty seconds, and I could continue to study that day with hardly any tinnitus. I developed this exercise by learning about Milton Erickson's utilisation technique (see p. 124). According to the Dream Lexicon, my left hand is my most dexterous part. This definition applies to my subconscious. This means that metaphorically my left hand has the same abilities as my subconscious. So the most dexterous part (which happens to be the part I have the most physical control over) becomes the part I have the most emotional control over. In this exercise, I visualise tinnitus as a physical object, a red ball. I imagine the red ball of tinnitus coming down from my left ear, down through the arm and into the palm of my left hand. At this point, I open and close my left hand while reminding the tinnitus that I am in control of it, but metaphorically, the subconscious is. This is because of the association already established between my subconscious and my left hand as being the same. I reinforce this by emphasising to the tinnitus that my subconscious is now in control of it, and I can open and close my hand at will, and the tinnitus often goes down at this point.

Fly-Tipping: A Simple Story

This exercise may seem like primary school work, but it was effective in my initial stages of treatment. It helped my subconscious get accustomed to opening up while beginning to learn to tidy away emotions and feelings and put them in their correct place, so they are easy to process. This happened through its engagement with a story it could identify with and relate to. Keith Oatley is an Anglo-Canadian novelist and professor emeritus of cognitive psychology at the University of Toronto who writes that "...the extent to which reading fictional texts elicits automatic retrieval of episodic memories and accompanying emotion..."[177] This may explain how and why the Fly-Tipping Story was effective in recovery. This exercise comprises a simple metaphorical narrative of my life but also includes the concept of fly-tipping. Essentially, tinnitus occurs when other people metaphorically fly-tip into your emotional space even without you realising it. This exercise reminds the subconscious to identify the emotions that originate from it and the negative emotional experiences which other people have given. It does not matter if these negative emotions are not realised consciously because this exercise is designed to work at the subconscious level. I use the metaphor of tidying up a house after people have fly-tipped to visualise this process and help the subconscious to follow this narrative.

I chose pictures from the internet without overthinking why one picture was more appealing to me than another to avoid conscious thought. This was done using the method of Focusing (see p. 208), but it is important that the pictures felt right at some level without analysing why this was the case.

I construct the story alongside choosing the pictures. The pictures that I choose are mostly simple and clear. So, for example, a typical house has a bathroom, kitchen, bedroom, living room, garden, attic and basement. I work with one room at a time. Take the kitchen, for example. A kitchen is where food is stored and prepared to be eaten. Since all the places in this story are oriented to supporting my emotions in various ways, in the Dream Lexicon, my subconscious has attributed a kitchen to be defined as "an emotional part of me where emotional nourishment is prepared". I first find a picture of a run-down and dirty kitchen which is not suitable for cooking in, and I find another picture of a well-done-up kitchen that appeals to me on some level. I put the two pictures on the page and write a simple descriptive story:

Photo by Lode Van de Veld

This was where I cooked my food for so many years and I can hardly believe that anyone could prepare food in this mess. After all, it is so important to have a clean area to prepare the food that nourishes me. In this kitchen, I felt no nourishment and everything I ate felt and tasted like polystyrene. It was no surprise that I could not find anything in the disorganised mess, not even the good, healthy stuff if I ever had it. No wonder I felt unwell most of the time!

Once I had removed all the stuff that was unnecessary and didn't belong there, the transformation was amazing. I had a floor again and also the motivation to cook and eat the stuff that is healthy and will make me strong. It is now easier for me to see what I have in order to prepare and eat it.

Photo by shche_ team onUnsplash

Photo by Luba Ertal

I found some old jars with spices in them while I was cleaning up the kitchen. They looked dirty and grubby. I hadn't used them for years. I gave them a good old wash and sprinkled some lavender on them, so the perfume would remind me that they were there. I carefully inspected each jar while putting fresh labels and contents in them. I now would be able to remember how to combine and use different spices in just the right manner in my cooking, taking care never to use too much or too little of the right spice, but just enough for that particular occasion.

In the examples above, I first described the kitchen as where emotional nourishment (food) is supposed to be prepared but explained that I became emotionally unwell because of the state of this kitchen. In the text accompanying the second image of the clean and done-up kitchen, I describe it as the opposite. This metaphor kickstarts a process where the subconscious can be reminded to tidy up and organise a part of itself.

303

One way this makes itself apparent is in my dreams, which usually happen on the same night.

I finally described having the jars of spices and how I put fresh spices in the bottles and then labelled them. I explain that I am able to combine spices in the right way and use the correct proportions. This metaphorical description symbolises how I can now measure the right emotions in the right amount, thereby using this metaphor to catalyse the subconscious to start doing this in the conscious world.

The example below is of the attic in the fly-tipping story.

"Gosh! What a mess, I haven't had a proper look around here for ages. No wonder, look at the state of it. I was wondering why my guests always wanted to come to the attic. I swear most of it is not mine, most of this junk. I wondered why my guests came with large bags  Photo by Kasman from Pixabay website *and left empty-handed, the penny has dropped. I have actually spotted something from when I was really young and a few of my teachers gave me some of this stuff when I was at school. It actually smells horrible in here."*

Photo by Conner Baker on Unsplash.com

In this example, I use the metaphor of a cluttered attic to illustrate how others in my special needs school passed on negative emotions to me and how these went directly into my subconscious without conscious detection. This is how I brought this awareness up to the conscious, where it becomes possible to engage with this notion on both levels.

"Wow! That is a lot better. I didn't know how big it was until all the junk had been cleared away and I had forgotten how beautiful natural wood looked. The window seems to let in more sunlight now. I also had a good sweep to make sure the last of the junk was gone. Not having my own and other people's junk in here has made a huge improvement."

Below is the description of a dream I had in the night immediately after I had done the above work on the Fly-Tipping Story.

Dream: *I was showing three or four people around the empty attic of my house (exactly like in the fly-tipping house). I was walking like I didn't have a disability. We were towards the front of the attic where the stairs went down and just talking casually. On the other side of the bare attic on the floor, there was a dark brown or black box towards the left of the attic. It was the size of a shoe box but a lot flatter, maybe half the height and I think it was made of wood. It had Johnny's things in it. I knew this without opening it.*

Johnny was my childhood sweetheart, who later passed away. This example shows how the story influenced my dream by demonstrating that the attic had been tidied up, with everything thrown away except for an essential item to me, which is why the subconscious did not dispose of it. The day after having this dream, the tinnitus was at 1, and I had a slight migraine. This could indicate that my subconscious was busy sorting out my metaphorical attic while dreaming.

The best way to sort out junk is to go through it and identify the separate categories it belongs to. I did this by identifying where it came from in the first place. Then, I recycled what could be used again for another purpose, ensuring I did not hoard what I did not need. In the attic that my subconscious had turned into a metaphor after everything had been cleared away, I first thought that the attic was empty as I was distracted by showing people around. However, the second time I looked, I saw the most important thing I had not thrown out; my memory of Johnny and what he gave me. The sunlight from the window forms a reflection on the attic floor; when I chose the picture, I overlooked this, but my subconscious made use of this. This is also a demonstration of the conscious not picking up detailed information, whereas the subconscious can do this, providing further insight into the dream.

I looked at this picture again and saw where the sun's reflection was on the floor; it was where I had noticed Johnny's box in the dream. Even though the box was black, indicating it was a dark time of my life, it now sat in the sunlight as it had always been, but I had never seen it. It was the only place where the sunlight fell on the attic floor. The other stuff was covering the box up and cluttering the floor, so I never noticed where the sunlight fell, but now that the attic was empty. I noticed the box in the sunlight, and I must have put it there when I was a child without emotional clutter. Surrounded by clutter, it remained there for so many years. I did not need anything in the attic except for the box of memories from Johnny. This meant that the clutter prevented me from realising that I had this box which is a part of me; like Johnny, this is not clutter, which is why it had not been thrown out. This will also help me to recognise my femininity as he did. Now that I can see the box clearly because it is the only thing in the attic, I can acknowledge the loss and the fact that Johnny and all the memories will always be with me.

The Fly-Tipping Story is versatile, and it is necessary to personalise it at every opportunity. Getting used to this concept was vital for the recovery from tinnitus; this way of working helped my subconscious to engage and play an active role in sorting out emotional clutter.

Chapter 19

Calming Exercises

Here are additional exercises that can bring a sense of calmness, often reducing tinnitus.

Body Relaxation

This exercise is the most effective in reducing tinnitus and works for me about ninety percent of the time. I concentrate on relaxing each part of my body, from my head to my toes. When I reach the top of my head, I go down inside and imagine relaxing the nerves, muscles, ligaments, tendons, the mind and the being. This process can be done numerous times, and I often used to do this at physiotherapy as well as every night before sleeping with David's recorded voice to guide me. This can also be done while imagining a soft, blue cloud from just above my head towards the top of my head while moving slowly to all parts of my body to my feet. There were times when the tinnitus would be between 2 and 4 when I woke up, I would do this exercise immediately, and it would often bring the tinnitus down to 1 or below, where it would remain for the whole day. This example demonstrates that even though I had tinnitus, it was possible to live daily without hearing the loud noise. I can do this exercise virtually anywhere and in nearly all situations, which makes this exercise reliable and versatile when others are not so effective.

The Cloud Of Relaxation

This exercise is a variation of the Body Relaxation Exercise and has a similar effect. I often do this when I feel the need to have a stronger visualisation than the previous exercise. I imagine a cloud of light blue above me that is just beginning to come down slowly on my head and just touching it and coming over my head and gently touching my face and eyes and nose, and it comes down over my neck and shoulders, and it shortly drifts down. Everywhere it touches, it brings a sense of calmness. It relaxes my muscles and makes me feel more comfortable as it continues its journey down my arms into my wrists and fingers. Everywhere it touches, it brings comfort and an experience of peacefulness. Some places benefit and relax quicker than others, and that is fine. The cloud continues its journey, taking all the time it needs to bring me a very strong experience of light blue peace and relaxation. It continues into my chest, stomach, hips, legs, my feet, all the way into the tips of my toes. This blue light goes deep inside to the centre of my being, where it meets a tiny seed of light blue light that has always been there and reminds it to awaken inside and that it has a job to do. I keep the light in my imagination, letting it touch and bring me peace.

The River Of Clarity

I imagine sitting by a river, gazing at the water as it rushes; the water is muddy and unclear, and I cannot see the river bed. As I watch, I see that the water ends up in a small river a few feet away. Here again, I cannot see the bottom of the river because the water remains unclear and muddy. I gaze down into the river for some time, not trying to see anything. I notice my body is relaxed, and my mind is calm and open. After some time, I begin to see my reflection in the water; this image of me looks like I have a face made of gold. After a while, this reflection changes into silver and then copper. As I gaze at my reflection while looking at the copper on my face instead of my skin, I notice cracks appearing on the copper itself, and it is as if my very face is cracking. At this point, I may continue with the Roads and Roundabouts exercise (see p. 173), or I could wait a little longer to see what else comes up, making a note of any thoughts, feelings and emotions at the same time. The first time I tried this exercise, the subsequent Automatic Writing came out stronger as if from a deeper source, making the tinnitus go down quicker than usual.

The Red Ball In The Rain

This was the first exercise David taught me. I have often done this if the Body Relaxation Exercise does not work. I imagine a small, red, sparkly ball and associate it with the sound in my ear. Next, I concentrate on making the connection between the ball and the sound strong enough to become one. I visualise this ball in the cool rain and watch as it slowly calms down and the sparks disappear. The sound often significantly reduces with this exercise, but I need to be in a calm environment with no distractions to make the image of the ball connect strongly to my tinnitus. For this exercise to be effective, it is essential that whatever object you imagine is a good fit to the sound of your tinnitus.

Dial Down

I imagine a clock with only one hand, and instead of the numbers going from 1 to 12, they go from 1 to 10. I put the hand at the number my tinnitus is at and imagine that the hand is moving down to a lower number. Sometimes the hand simply moves in between two numbers, and I wait until it is ready to move down a little further. It is important not to force the hand down; it should instead go down gently with the mind. If this is impossible, I imagine putting a little olive oil in the centre to help the hand move more freely. On one occasion, with this exercise, my tinnitus went down from 3 to 2. Even though this may not sound like a huge improvement, a slight reduction in the sound of tinnitus makes a big difference to my quality of life in the moment.

Point Of Light Expanding From Abdomen

This exercise is not aimed at reducing tinnitus. However, it lets me feel calm in the moment, which can positively affect tinnitus. One day, people around me were stressed and angry, and the tinnitus was at 4. As I have mentioned elsewhere, the events in my immediate environment significantly influenced my tinnitus, making me vulnerable to other people's negative emotions. This was when I needed to feel calm, but it was often the most challenging time to feel this way. The following exercise is designed to help me to feel a sense of calmness where I am not in control of what is happening because the environment is stressful.

I imagine a point of beautiful white light right at the centre of my abdomen. As I watch, this tiny point of light expands upwards into my chest, downwards into my legs, and sideways into my arms. Slowly, the point of light encircles me, growing even bigger to encircle three feet of space around me. I feel safe and secure in this beautiful white sphere since whatever is happening on the outside of the sphere remains on the outside and cannot enter my immediate vicinity.

The River And Its Stones

There were times when my tinnitus was loud, and I also felt that my emotions were stuck and not flowing due to an emotional blockage that was hard to identify. This exercise is beneficial if the unexpressed emotions are too big and cannot be moved easily. Often when I do this exercise, the tinnitus goes down gradually, and it feels like something internal is becoming unblocked.

I imagine strolling by a river on a warm and sunny day, and I gaze at the water as it flows by me. The river is not wide at all, and the water is clear enough to see the river bed with its beautiful fish going about their business being fish. My feet are bare as I wander along this beautiful river's path, and the cool grass feels so nice under my feet. I wander this way for some time, gazing as the sunlight dances across the water, and it feels like there are diamonds where the sunlight and the water meet. Suddenly, I see a row of large stones forming a perfect line from one river bank to the other, right across the water. As I watch, the water builds up before the line of stones. I notice that hardly any water is flowing on the other side, and there is much pressure on this side. I carefully step into the river, slowly remove the stones one at a time, and safely put them on the river bank. As I do this, I feel the water flowing free on the other side of the line of stones, and I also observe how the water now moves down the river with grace and ease. At this point, the tinnitus usually goes down. I notice how the fish that were once confined to only a part of this beautiful river are now free to enjoy it in its entirety. The water now gently slows down and seems calmer, as if it now knows that it is certain of meeting its destiny, the sea, and that it can take all the time in the world to get there now that it is free.

The Smoke of Silence

Sometimes, I would have tinnitus, which would give me a headache. These times were difficult for me mentally and physically. On one particular occasion, the tinnitus was at 3. It would often be the case where the sound could not be associated with a metaphor that I could manipulate using hypnosis. So here is what I did; I imagined a bonfire in my belly. Smoke is usually light grey, which is 'soothing and calming' in the Dream Lexicon. I imagined this smoke from the bonfire slowly rising into my chest, going through my neck, my face, my head and finally to my ears as it brought calmness to the tinnitus, reducing it in volume to 1. This exercise is particularly effective when the tinnitus is dispersed over my head, and it becomes difficult to identify a specific area. This exercise was also effective when the tinnitus brought on a headache that would disappear in time.

From an Acorn to an Oak

This exercise helped me to distance myself from tinnitus, which meant that I heard it either not so loud or not at all. I came up with this exercise when I learnt that this could be applied to physical pain; when people can distance themselves from pain, they feel it less. I imagine I am in a park or a forest and see an acorn on the ground by my feet. The tinnitus is a red ball on the ground beside it, looking large and looming. I imagine standing on the acorn, and as I do this, the acorn grows into a tree, carrying me higher with it until I find myself standing on the top of an oak tree. As I look down from the top of the tree, the tinnitus is hardly visible beneath me, which is when the tinnitus reduces in volume.

Turn Yourself Into Silence

So much of what I write about in this book would be disagreeable to medical professionals. The following exercise would be particularly unbelievable and may sound ridiculous, but it works; this is why I offer it here. It is a simple exercise where I give the tinnitus a specific instruction of what it needs to do by thinking: "Tinnitus, go down and turn yourself into silence." When I undertake this exercise, I need to feel confident enough to do this and to feel a respectful but slight feeling of authority over my tinnitus. More often than not, the tinnitus reduces in volume; if I think about these words a few times, the tinnitus disappears. One explanation is that tinnitus is the production of sound because of emotional suppression. The sound is present and does not seem to know what to do with itself except make sound. I can reduce the sound I hear by giving it an explicit instruction. This did not work for most of my recovery, only in the latter period. This could be because the subconscious had processed all the emotions already, which is why the tinnitus could have been receptive to this instruction. Sometimes, even when the tinnitus was at 4, it went down to 1 or below when I did this exercise.

Taking Stock - The Mountains Exercise

When we are close to completing a long and tiring journey, we often forget to look back to see where we have come from, but when we do, this helps us to acknowledge the journey we have undertaken and how far we have come. Recovering from tinnitus was the most arduous journey I have ever embarked upon, so it was good to take some time to reflect on how I had come so far. In this exercise, I asked my subconscious to consolidate and summarise the main mountains I had to cross before arriving at silence. To do this, I used Focusing to choose a photograph of a mountain range to work with. My subconscious also chose the number of summits in the picture.

I looked at each while writing automatically, which led the subconscious to identify the main issues I had to address. This provided an overview of the problems which led me to have tinnitus, and since this was done towards the end of my recovery, I did not need to explore these issues in detail. It was a way of acknowledging and reflecting on my journey to silence.

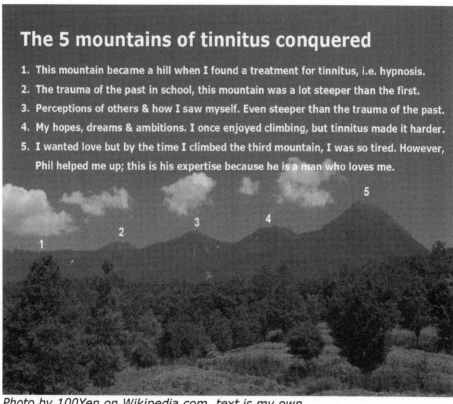

The 5 mountains of tinnitus conquered

1. This mountain became a hill when I found a treatment for tinnitus, i.e. hypnosis.

2. The trauma of the past in school, this mountain was a lot steeper than the first.

3. Perceptions of others & how I saw myself. Even steeper than the trauma of the past.

4. My hopes, dreams & ambitions. I once enjoyed climbing, but tinnitus made it harder.

5. I wanted love but by the time I climbed the third mountain, I was so tired. However, Phil helped me up; this is his expertise because he is a man who loves me.

Photo by 100Yen on Wikipedia.com, text is my own

Part F - Practising Silence

Chapter 20

The Home Stretch Of Returning To Silence

This chapter tells the narrative of the final leg of the journey to permanent silence. I explain a new way of living that anchors my daily experience in emotional reality, allowing me to feel the emotions necessary for the recovery from tinnitus and the maintenance of experiencing silence. It will also enunciate the need to acknowledge my deepest desires and how this helped me change my lifestyle to recognise what I actually wanted emotionally. I was nearly there and could see the summit of the mountain. Silence was only half a yard away, but this particular part of the journey left me exhausted, unfocused, and unable to concentrate. Even then, it was worth it. I found it difficult to express what I was going through to anyone else since I knew they would not understand. How can one feel like they have travelled for a lifetime while appearing to continue with business as usual? This chapter highlights examples in my life that increased tinnitus and my coping strategies for reducing tinnitus when emotional trigger points make tinnitus louder. Finally, I will also explain how my best friend was crucial to my recovery and helped me to complete my journey.

The end of my journey into recovery from tinnitus was not a smooth process. It was full of mountains, sometimes hills, and occasionally flat ground. From the journal I kept, it is evident that silence was a real possibility in the future, but events needed to happen between then and now. Some occurred naturally, and I initiated some. However, when the conditions of the subconscious were right, silence came and with it, the wisdom of learning what was right for me, not necessarily what I wanted at a conscious level or what I expected but what I needed emotionally and with this, happiness followed.

I had a dream on the 2nd of June 2017, but I had no recollection. I had been noting my dreams down over the last six years, since June 2011. On this particular day, I wanted to recall the dream using Automatic Writing, but my subconscious said this was a false dream and I should not write it down. Since my tinnitus was 1.5 compared to being at 4 the previous day, I knew that this was another turning point in my recovery. I did not need to analyse dreams which I had done daily over the last six years. My suspicions were confirmed when I had the following hypnagogia the next day, and the tinnitus was at 1.

Someone put my azure blue hoodie on me and then said " bye Sapna" as they left the room.

It seemed as if the hypnagogia was telling me that my dream analysing part had ended by bidding farewell to the conscious part of me playfully.

The following are accounts of various experiences on the final leg of my journey. Although personal, I acknowledge that some readers might face similar situations when tinnitus is still too difficult to manage without these exercises and the assistance of hypnosis. I provide anecdotes of personal experiences and how I overcame them using the exercises outlined in this book.

Things That Increased the Volume of Tinnitus

Some factors increase tinnitus, like being in a stressful environment. Even though I had learnt to reduce tinnitus at these times, this was not always the case, but this improved with practice.

Processing Strong Emotions

The most important factor was my ability to be aware of negative emotions in my immediate environment and to prevent these from entering me and changing my current calm equilibrium.

For example, an argument would occur in another room that had no relationship to me, increasing my tinnitus. The way I learnt to deal with this was to imagine a light pink bubble around me which protected me from all that went on externally to it. This bubble was from my imagination and something I created, which gave me the power to stop things in my environment that I had no control over from affecting my tinnitus, returning the control to me (see p. 101). So in time, I learnt to process these emotions that did not originate from me, and in this way, they would pass through me without increasing my tinnitus.

Next is an example of how other people caused stress that affected my tinnitus.

The Tinnitus has been at 2 today and I'm not sure whether it is because of spending time with Kathleen yesterday who was stressed out and behaved weird or because it's the last day of my period. I have had a slight headache towards the evening, there was stress again in the evening with someone on the phone while I ate dinner.

I had a new Personal Assistant who was stressed, and her stress manifested in her behaviour and manner. Even though I was not the cause of this stress, this increased my tinnitus and maintained it at a constant level throughout the day. This demonstrates that other people can affect stress and tinnitus, which made me vulnerable. At the time, I had not quite mastered the art of completely protecting myself, though I could achieve this most of the time through hypnosis.

The following example demonstrates that the subconscious requires time to process these emotions after an event where strong emotions are involved, whether negative or positive. This can happen over one night of dreaming or over several nights. Sometimes it is helpful to do Automatic Writing exercises, while at other times, the subconscious needs to be left alone. In either case, my subconscious always tells me what to do.

I woke up late today at around 9.30 am because my tinnitus was loud and it was driving me mad as it was at 4 but I knew that my subconscious has a lot to process from last weekend so while it was torture, I wasn't worried. I did some more Focusing this morning and the tinnitus is going down slowly. The Focusing was about being in hell but then having Phil. The Automatic Writing at the end told me that this is the end of tinnitus and for once I believe this because of spending so much time with Phil last weekend and dancing with him and sitting with him on the boat. I don't feel well at all today and listened to some calming and relaxing music which helped a bit. The tinnitus is around 1.5 now which is the quietest it's been all week.

This happened after Phil's wedding, where I was the Best Man. What is important to note here is that the positive experience consciously brought up unfamiliar emotions. These had a dramatic effect subconsciously, but one which elicited positive emotional changes deep down in the subconscious, which was long-lasting. This was why I was not concerned with the tinnitus being so loud.

Not Enough Sleep

This example demonstrates the importance of being able to sleep, thereby having the opportunity to dream. When sleep is interrupted, so is dreaming, and this often dramatically affects the tinnitus the next day. In most cases, undertaking Automatic Writing the following day would enable the rest of the emotions to be processed, dramatically reducing tinnitus.

I didn't sleep much last night and I am not sure why but I think I felt restless and trapped. I woke up at around 3:30 am again and couldn't sleep for a while but managed to sleep for a bit after this. I am feeling unwell today, very tired, fed up and very trapped physically and mentally but at least I have identified the emotions. The tinnitus is around 3 and my stomach hurts but who cares?

Being unable to sleep often means that the conscious cannot relax enough to relinquish control to the subconscious. It is beneficial to write automatically at these times to keep tinnitus low. In this example, despite not sleeping, it was possible to keep the tinnitus at 1 while simultaneously understanding what my subconscious needed to express.

Before sleeping last night, I did a few lines of Automatic Writing. I woke up at around 5 am and I was not able to sleep even though my tinnitus was at 1 and I felt awake but tired. I listened to the meditations recorded by David but couldn't get back to sleep. So I continued with the same Automatic Writing until my subconscious told me to stop Automatic Writing. I was able to sleep after this and after listening to the meditations. I had to wake up at 8:15 am because my morning carer had to go early today. After breakfast, I continued the Automatic Writing until once again my subconscious told me to stop. I noticed that even though I had woken up in the night, the tinnitus didn't go higher than 1. Maybe the message in the Automatic Writing was important for my conscious to acknowledge, which is why it may not have turned into a dream as I don't analyse dreams anymore. However, this time, maybe the subconscious had a message that it wanted me to acknowledge consciously. The Automatic Writing was about emotions being like ghosts from the past which need acknowledgement from the conscious so that they could vanish and not bang on the walls of the subconscious.

From time to time, the subconscious has an important message for the conscious, which it knows cannot be put in a dream because the period of Dream Analysis has ended. The subconscious then uses Automatic Writing as an alternative way of conveying its message to the conscious. If the conscious does not initiate Automatic Writing or acknowledge messages in other ways, the tinnitus will become louder. This is why I must continue to write automatically in my daily life.

Interrupted During Dreaming

Even after my recovery, and while I was recovering, it was important for the time that I was dreaming not to be disrupted. The tinnitus would become loud when a dream was interrupted, as the message from the subconscious was incomplete. This is because the subconscious needs to dream to process emotions. There came a time when having enough dreams was sufficient to maintain my tinnitus at 1 or below.

The doorbell rang at 8:00 am which woke me up with a start. Unfortunately I was in the middle of a dream and so the tinnitus was at 3 probably because of this. I just feel completely exhausted today and don't know whether I am coming or going. I did Focusing and the tinnitus went down slowly.

In this example, I did Focusing on waking to help the subconscious process the rest of the emotions that should have been expressed as dreams but were cut short.

Not Acknowledging The Subconscious In The Moment

This is an example where the tension between the opposing desires of my conscious and subconscious increased the tinnitus until my subconscious provided instructions on what to do to get it down. I was in bed the night before my birthday. My tinnitus had been at 4 all day. Even though I was planning to see two friends the next day, I did not want to tell them about my birthday since my conscious was resistant to anyone knowing about it, owing to my negative associations with it.

I don't know what is going on today. I woke up exhausted and the tinnitus was at 4 so there is something happening in my subconscious mind. I did Focusing and the tinnitus went down to 2 and it is very slowly going down ever since Focusing. The Focusing was about acknowledging the tiring and long journey that I have undertaken but which no one knows about. Sent a message to Phil telling him that it is my birthday tomorrow. Immediately after sending this, my tinnitus went down from 4 to 1 in a few minutes demonstrating that this was a big issue that my subconscious needed to deal with here and now.

Even though I have many close friends, I have ensured that they do not know when my birthday is so that I do not have to celebrate it or be reminded of it by them wishing me a happy birthday. In this example, my birthday was on a day that Phil took me swimming (we went most Fridays before the Coronavirus pandemic as it helps my disability), but I had decided not to tell him so that I could enjoy myself in the water with him. My tinnitus was at 4, and I woke up in the middle of the night the day before. As usual, I wrote automatically to see what my subconscious wanted me to acknowledge. My subconscious instructed me to tell Phil immediately that it was my birthday the next day and that I felt down about it. As soon as the message was sent, my tinnitus went down from 4 to 1. Until then, I had equated my birthday with the difficulties of my birth, which caused me to have Cerebral Palsy. My subconscious aimed to ensure that I associated my birthday with a positive and happy event. In this case, my subconscious helped me make new and positive memories of my birthday, which made me happy rather than depressed.

Period

When I first had tinnitus, and for many years after beginning my treatment with David, the sound would be deafening (between 7 and 8) with the onset of my period, and the noise lasted for about ten days. Prior to having tinnitus, I experienced premenstrual tension (PMT), which stopped with the onset of tinnitus. This led me to assume that the extra emotions from this time, which I should have consciously felt, instead expressed themselves by contributing to the noise. At these times, I felt more numb than usual, as PMT created strong emotions that were impossible to get to the conscious level.

Even though I was good at hypnosis through what David had taught me, there was little I could do to bring the tinnitus down during these times. These were extremely difficult times, which made me feel suicidal. The headaches were constant because of the loud tinnitus. As I learnt to work with dreams, I discovered the excellent benefits of hypnagogia which I tried to include, especially at these times. I also wrote automatically for most of the day. These helped to some degree in eventually bringing the tinnitus down, where it averaged between 5 and 8 for the duration of my period. In the last year of recovery, these times have not been so bad, and I have been able to sit up and study. This is mainly because the tinnitus has dramatically reduced, in general, due to the process of analysing dreams, Automatic Writing, and my friendship with Phil.

Emotional Residue

The next example demonstrates the difference between tinnitus and residue.

It's 9 am and the tinnitus is at 3 or 4. I've just listened to the recorded meditation. I couldn't sleep for some of the night because the tinnitus was too loud. My tinnitus is now going down very slowly I think and it feels lighter. It feels like it might disappear in around 15 minutes or the next time I use the loo [when I would do the Bladder Exercise].

Often when the dreams were extremely vivid or the Automatic Writing was particularly powerful, my tinnitus would go down on its own over a matter of hours. This is because it was noise without an emotional connection, just like the ringing in your ears after a gunshot. It is similar to hearing an echo, which lasts after the original sound has ebbed and takes some time before it finally disappears. This was also the case when I no longer needed to analyse dreams. The tinnitus would be there when I woke up, but it would sound weak even though loud and would disappear over a short period. (For more information on emotional residue, see p. 260)

Stress And Uncertainty

This is an example where the tinnitus was loud because of being in a difficult situation where my plans were in jeopardy.

The tinnitus has been at 3 all day and I couldn't do any Automatic Writing or Focusing. Yesterday was stressful since my external hard drive was wiped by mistake and I lost all the interview trials for the Ph.D., but found the DVDs which might work. I just need to remember that there is nothing more important than Phil's love and friendship and that there was a good chance that tinnitus would have killed me. This is how I make sure that I put everything in perspective.

Even though the feelings of stress and uncertainty originated in the subconscious, what is important here is that I can identify the sources of my stress and the feeling of uncertainty. In this way, I remain connected to my feelings at both conscious and subconscious levels, even though they are sometimes unpleasant. As a result, tinnitus remains low in the long term.

Chapter 21

Conclusion

I would like to conclude by explaining the immense joy I experience through the love and friendship that Phil and I share and how this bond has proven vital in my recovery. Finally, it is time for me to move on and learn to live rather than survive.

I owe my life to my incredible teacher and hypnotherapist, David Corr and his knowledge of hypnosis, who set me on the journey of my recovery from a debilitating condition, one which medical professionals do not understand. I was not an ordinary client, and David is far from ordinary in his profound understanding of applied hypnosis.

I hope this book rebuts the misguided perceptions of hypnosis. Yapko elaborates,

> "Hypnosis invites lively discussion, curious speculation, and even profound philosophizing about the nature of human consciousness and the complex, often confusing relationships among mind, body and spirit. Hypnosis continues to

confound a general public that can't readily grasp how it can be used in cheesy stage show routines yet also be taken seriously by prominent researchers and clinicians who unequivocally declare it an effective vehicle of treatment."[178]

Our subconscious is a part of us, but simultaneously, it is not within our immediate reach. So it is little wonder that conditions like tinnitus are written off as untreatable by the medical establishment, which often does not recognise that we are physical beings and people with psychological and emotional experiences. We carry our emotional experiences throughout our lives, while we remain unaware of what they consist of, and sometimes these become too heavy for us to bear.

Hypnosis provides a solution to this, a way of recognising the whole of us and how we have become the people we are today.

This book demonstrates that my journey was personally significant, and I have completed it, but I am aware that many still have tinnitus. Therefore, in sharing the words in this book, I hope others in similar situations will take their own journeys and experience silence that comes from emotional tranquillity.

If you remember me today

You will forget me tomorrow

For your mind breaks like shattered glass in your hands

But I don't understand why pieces of glass are running through my

veins

I lost something of myself a long time ago when the time was lost like

memories on a summer's day

I forgot what I should have remembered that day

But I couldn't remember the events that happened yesterday

I ran in the forest with bare feet

But still

I couldn't remember

I had lost everything

But I couldn't remember what I had lost

And then I came upon a river and looked down at my reflection

And then I remembered what I had forgotten a long time ago

That I was free to be me

Epilogue

I was nearly there but was not there yet. It is a funny thing how sometimes what happens is stranger than fiction. By no stretch of my imagination could I have consciously come up with the events I describe here, but my subconscious had other ideas.

I had considerably improved some years after my last hypnotherapy session and kept up with my hypnosis exercises, acknowledging my subconscious daily. I had done everything that I could possibly think of to hear silence, but it did not come permanently. I was frustrated and did not know how to take that last step into permanent silence.

So one day, my subconscious came up with a plan. The plan was based on the fact that I am opposed to lying and would never tell a lie, especially to Phil, my best friend. My subconscious instructed me (through Automatic Writing) to set up a time and a date to meet with Phil and tell him that I had recovered from tinnitus when I was still hearing the noise. It instructed me to buy a butterfly dress when it knew I did not wear dresses at all and that I should wear it when I met Phil. Throughout my treatment, I used the butterfly metaphor to symbolise gaining silence, since it signified a complete and irreversible transformation. As well as the dress, my subconscious also said to buy a butterfly clip for my hair. The tinnitus was loud that day, but as soon as I left the shop with the clip, the tinnitus almost disappeared. This small but significant act indicated that something big and extraordinary was about to happen and that I was preparing for it.

The next task I was instructed to do was to write a letter to Phil and set up a date to give him the letter. The letter needed to contain a summary of everything I had been through to recover from tinnitus and finally to mention that I did not have tinnitus anymore. My subconscious knew I was not accustomed to discussing my problems with friends, not even with close friends like Phil. This was another challenge it wanted me to overcome, and it went on to detail the substance of the letter and approved it after it was written consciously. I felt desperately foolish in writing such a letter because I could still hear the tinnitus while writing about how I had recovered from it. The letter was dated the 6th of June 2018, when Phil and I arranged to meet. This was also the date that my subconscious had turned into a deadline for my tinnitus to go. It was nerve-wracking, but I had worked with my subconscious enough to trust it to guide me implicitly.

On the 6th of June 2018, I met Phil outside a cafe close to where we usually meet with our other friends. I had already told him I had something important to say, asking to see him alone. When we met at the cafe, he chatted about random stuff, and by this point, I was too nervous to take in what he was saying. He finally asked me what I wanted to tell him and said I looked nice in my butterfly dress. I could not speak and handed the letter to him. He took his time to read it carefully. He said he was happy that I had recovered from tinnitus, but Phil did not feel he played a part in it and that I should take all the credit. I suspected Phil would say something like this since he is not in the habit of taking credit for his actions and because love comes naturally to him. However, he did not fully realise the implications of how

331

he had helped me recover from tinnitus.

When the tinnitus returned a few days after I met with Phil, I challenged my subconscious on why this was the case and why it had made me lie to my best friend. It said I was incapable of lying, and at this point, I was confused and disappointed.

What had happened in my act of giving Phil the letter while wearing the butterfly dress was that I had subconsciously set up a situation where on the one hand, I had told Phil that the tinnitus was gone and, on another, it was against my nature to tell a lie, especially to someone I loved. This situation had backed my tinnitus into a corner. Tinnitus as a part of my subconscious returned because it needed to express how it felt about this situation, and after that, the emotional suppression ended for good.

This journey has ended for me, and on a glorious sunny day on the 8th of August 2019, I wore my beautiful butterfly dress again and a chain and pendant of the tree of life that Phil and Lucy, his wife, gave me one Christmas. I met my friend Phil in the park. We decided to do a little private ceremony all on our own. We burnt tinnitus by burning a letter that I had written to my past in which I highlighted all that had gone wrong. I acknowledged Phil and David's role in this epic journey

of mine, and then Phil read a beautiful poem. We buried the ashes under an oak tree.

Thus, the time has come to say goodbye to an era of torture and terror because, with love, I knew that tinnitus would not last. In this new life, I want to make every moment as joyful as possible.

Recovery was destined for me, and it took hypnosis and love in the right amount for me to return to silence again. In writing this book, I thank David and Phil, for silence would have been impossible without either, but love makes all things possible.

Acknowledgements

I wish to thank my amazing family for their love, support and encouragement while writing and publishing this book. I also would like to express my heartfelt thanks to Prof. Lizbeth Goodman and Prof. Cahal McLaughlin, my Ph.D. supervisors, for their enormous consideration and patience when I was too unwell to study for my Ph.D. and for supporting me and making the time with them stress-free.

I would also like to thank my wonderful friends, Andy Rushton, Patricia Rogers, David Miller, Mary Grove, Debra Hinton, Stella Dessoy, Phil Walder and Varsha Dadlani, for their insights and perspective on my words.

Appendix

Dialogue With Denial

Sapna: Hello Denial I wish to talk to you today about the reason that you prevent me from entering my subconscious and why exactly are you guarding it.

Denial: Because Sophia is down there without a care don't you know that and I want to protect her because she is weak and you know that don't you Sapna because she is as vulnerable as you are and she will never go far without me you see and in this way I protect her in a shell for she is a stranger to your way of life and I don't need to think twice about looking after her anymore because I'm full of hope for you in order to live without her you must fly away from here.

Sapna: Don't you think I can protect her once she comes up to the surface and out into the sunlight beyond this cave?

Denial: No you are wrong Sophia is strong but she is full of woe because the past has been rotten to her she is a slave in my cave I keep her safe and warm she is fine with me down here and I don't want you coming near me anymore and spoiling everything for me you see I'm her destiny it is bad enough that you have dreams Sophia but I am rotten to the core and I don't want you interfering once more so go away from here my dear Sapna you have no responsibility to come here.

Sapna: I acknowledge the past has been rotten to her but Sophia is strong enough to come up to the surface and she can begin to learn about how to live a full emotional life. I'm not going anywhere until I take her out of this cave with me. She also misses Jack.

Denial: You can stay here as long as you want Sophia is not going anywhere for the world will abuse her once more and I can't have that can I even though she wants to fly I tether her to the ground and she is safe inside my cave Jack is brave for coming here and trying his luck but even he can't get through to me even though he tries hard poor man.

Sapna: What if I make a direct promise to you, Denial, that I will look after Sophia and keep her safe but at the same time teach her to live in the world beyond this cave? Can you hand Sophia over to me?

Denial: No way just go away you are not wanted here anymore Sapna because you will spoil her rotten now she is alive safe inside my cave where nobody goes and she is not polluted by life things are fine as they are and as they stand why don't you go away from here now my dear Sapna I won't let her through to you so go away from here and finally go up a gear with something else on your plate for I can't waste time with you on my mind.

Sapna: I am stopping this dialogue here with you Denial. This is because I am hungry but you can be sure that I will return to talk to you today or tomorrow for as long as it takes to get Sophia up to the surface but I want to respectfully understand you. See you later or tomorrow.

The next day

Sapna: I am back to talk some more with you Denial and I would like your attention. What exactly are you afraid will happen to Sophia when she comes up to the surface and out of this cave? Notice; I use the word when rather than if.

Denial: Well Sophia my darling one if she comes out of this cave she will misbehave and Denial keeps her safe here for she has forgotten to live a normal life so I want to protect her in a bubble surrounding her with love and warmth and I can't guarantee you will do that for Sapna is full of dreams and they can't come true because they have already had come true in the past and you cannot guarantee that can you I am smiling at you now Sophia I don't know what else to say really except go away.

Sapna: Don't you think, Denial, it is better to be aware of the truth of one's past rather than living your whole life with someone like you? If Sophia has the opportunity to put the pain of the past behind her which is where it actually belongs, she would live a full emotional life from here on from this point forward. Pain is temporary, life is permanent.

Denial: No Sophia is wrong to go out there I'm telling you Sapna Denial is comfortable and warm Denial won't break your heart Denial means put the music on and listen to it Denial needs you to understand when I'm awake you are asleep and that is why I'm uniquely yours to deny I'm afraid Sophia is staying right here with me now and you can forget coming back for her again.

Sapna: I am afraid, Denial, I have to remind you of something very important, this is, I have been seeing David for four years now and I have just finished therapy in December. I was his apprentice all this time and I have learnt wisely from him. To deny emotional life is wrong, to deny what I feel is wrong, I have also learnt to feel what Sophia feels when she is stuck in a cage and you put her there. Heartbreaks come and go, recovery is quick and learning is enormous. It is about turning off the music and allowing her to listen to the tiny voice right in the centre of her in the quiet, in the stillness and in the calmness of an empty mind.

Denial: To deny is to feel bliss for Sophia and you can be rude about life but she won't mind for she is warm and comfortable in my bed fed on wine all the time she is so divine but she doesn't know the truth about life and what it holds for her I'm not sure what to do to convince you that denying is right and you can put that torch away now I don't like its light it's too bright stinging in my eyes there is no disguise from it you are not very wise.

Sapna: Denial, I will end this conversation here today and continue talking to you tomorrow. I respect your views but they are wrong. See you tomorrow and thank you for your time.

The next day

Sapna: Hello Denial, I'm back today to continue our conversation. Could you tell me what you see when you look at yourself in a full-length mirror?

Denial: I see black and white you are wrong and I am right I have a wise old forehead and a cloak made of satin or silk my eyes are brought together and not far apart and I won't break your heart like the last man did and you know who that is don't you Sophia Jackson is entrapped in a cage but when you turn the light on she is not there because she has vanished into thin air and I despair for her you know out there but it isn't fair to take her away from me I don't like your company any more Sapna.

Sapna: Where has Sophia gone? Whether or not we like each other is not important but the welfare of Sophia is, and that is why I'm here. Tell me Denial, what do you want in return for Sophia? And why are you afraid of my torch?

Denial: I don't like the light on anyway it illuminates shadows that I can't see normally and I don't like that because I'm afraid of the dark and the light I like the colour grey it's boring and dull I must confess I'm not the best dressed guy in town but I'm not the worst either you must mark me either way for I'm Denial I'm here to stay.

Sapna: Well, Denial when small children don't like a certain food but it's good for them, they are encouraged to have a tiny amount at a time. Eventually they like the taste of the once forbidden food, they are encouraged to play with it, to enjoy it, to have fun with it. I wonder Denial could we try this experiment together if I hold your hand and keep you safe and calm? For example in my pocket I have got Approval and I would like to break a tiny bit off for you to try.

Denial: OK then I want to touch the sky can I see it first at last what does it look like? What does it taste like? Why do I fear this example of mine? How kind of you to offer me this I will try a bit now here I go why does it make my rivers flow? Why does it melt in my mouth? I want out why does it taste so divine all the time? I'm confused about my own feelings about this I have never tasted food like this it has blown me away but it's okay for now.

Sapna: Well done Denial, I'm proud of you. How do you feel? I really do like the taste of Approval myself and I think for you its a big positive step. How do you feel and do you have any concerns about Approval?

Denial: When I was younger I didn't like it at all but I was not designed for that type of thing I've got colour in my cheeks now as I look in the mirror yes I like Approval very much can I have some more?

Sapna: I have as much as you want, please take it from me with my love. I'm really happy at your progress Denial.

Denial: Please take my hand as I try it once again and I will count to 10 and will swallow it down whole here I go now I'm up for a laugh I'm not in the dark anymore because of you Sapna thank you very much for letting me go I appreciate your time I feel divine all the time.

Sapna: My pleasure Denial and I'm proud of you. I will have to say bye bye now but you know what to do. I will be back tomorrow to try another emotional nourishment with you but in the meantime take some more Approval and experiment and play with it in your mouth and then swallow it while acknowledging how you feel about it.

The next day

Sapna: Hello Denial, I am back to talk to you today. How are you? And what were your experiences about tasting Approval?

Denial: Well Sapna I liked it very much and it was not rough on my tongue I am used to it now and my light burns brighter for it yes it's tasty that Approval and I like that taste on my tongue I am stronger for it you know and my powers of denying grow weak with every breath I take so thank you Sapna very much for that treat.

Sapna: My pleasure Denial, my enormous pleasure. I have more Approval if you want to nourish yourself with it. I was wondering if you had any questions about Approval and if you would like to try another treat from my pocket.

Denial: One step at a time Sapna we can't rush these things you know I would like to wait a while before I try another sweet we could try it tomorrow if you like same one or another variety of sweet I don't mind Sapna because you are new to me I like meeting you this way it's okay to be in dismay all this time because life is not like that a bed of roses for there are thorns underneath them if you look hard enough but I have had enough of their stuff and you Sophia what about you I am through with this life how about you?

Sapna: I am so fed up about the noise in my ear and all those emotions falling through the crack between the subconscious and the conscious at the entrance to this cave. I wonder Denial, could you help me here or do you need to change your name first?

Denial: I will wait because the transformation hasn't completed yet I need to eat all your sweets for that to happen I will wait and take my time then but I won't count to ten I will tell you when I am ready for the next one which is not today I know you are in dismay.

Sapna: Okay Denial, no problem at all, take your time and I will ask you whether you are ready for the next sweet every time we talk. I will have to go now but I will be back tomorrow. In the meantime can you consider how to keep my tinnitus low, I will appreciate this very much. See you tomorrow.

The next day

Sapna: Hello Denial how are you today? How do you feel today?

Denial: I am okay today I guess I liked Approval very much can I try another one of a different variety and maybe we can make that gap smaller now could I try Agreement instead before I go back to bed and wake up the next morning I would like to try this one more time because I tried Agreement before and I didn't want it anymore because it tasted nasty at the time one more time I tried it and it didn't work it drove me berserk I was ill in bed for a week but I was not unique five hundred times I said no in my lifetime but they didn't listen to me you see they spoiled my destiny and I am not having that any more so I backed away from Agreement like there was no tomorrow.

Sapna: Yes I totally understand your situation and I think Agreement only tastes sweet when you have it on your own terms and how and when you want it and when it is appropriate. Because too much Agreement all the time is bad for the system but too little is harmful too. Denial you are the only one who can decide what is the right amount for you at any given moment in time. So, Denial are you ready for Agreement the second sweet in my pocket which I present to you with my love.

Denial: Yes I am ready for Agreement Sapna once I have eaten this sweet I will consider it more let me have it now please if you don't mind I can't wait to feel so divine.

Sapna: Here is Agreement from my pocket for you with my love. Look how bright and shiny it is, even in this cave and it is tasty too. Let it melt in your mouth and you will know what to do.

Denial: Why thank you for the sweet Sapna I will take it with my tea it tastes so divine all the time to me I have swallowed it down Sophia I am just letting you know thank you Sapna I will let you go until tomorrow when we meet again and then we can talk some more about Agreement and then maybe that gap will close even more now that I have had that sweet I feel uniquely in control of myself now and forever.

Sapna: Well done Denial I am proud of you once again for eating the sweet of Agreement. I think we should leave it here for now because you need time to digest Agreement like you did with Approval and feel it in your body, notice where it is and how it moves and how it becomes absorbed by your bloodstream. Bye for now, talk to you again tomorrow.

The next day

Sapna: Hello Denial, how are you? And I would love to know how you have been managing with Agreement in your system. Could you describe how you feel so I may acknowledge your feelings too?

Denial: I agree with Agreement very much and how it melts in my mouth and how it resonates with me a unique kind of destiny where my rivers flow into the sea of tranquillity and you know that gap it has closen now and I promise you Sophia will be up soon up by the crack of dawn by the light of the morning for she is down there in despair I can feel that resonating in my body and I don't need to tell anybody the good news but only to you because you are there without a care and I thank you for your time in denying me Sapna but I am a new man and I can have a plan for the future I will bring her up when she is ready to come up.

Sapna: Thank you so much Denial, this is wonderful news. Would you like another sweet which is the sweet of Sanction? This is important because it gives permission for you to feel what is true rather than not allowing you to acknowledge your feelings whether good or bad because you have to Sanction both equally to come through.

Denial: Sanction means permission right but I am Denial yes okay I will have some of that then I will Sanction myself to have one and then I will see the fires of the fireworks lighting up the sky at night for I am blue without you Sophia as I met Jack he told me this along the way to brighten his day but Denial denied everything that day in the month of May it was cold and windy that day but Denial denies everything you say.

Sapna: Well I used to say that but not any more you are changing Denial, I am sure and I am over the moon about it. Right, the sweet sweet of Sanction is coming your way. I have it in my pocket today for you. Once again put it in your mouth and let it melt and see how you feel tomorrow about eating this sweet.

Denial: Why thank you Sapna ever so much for this sweet sweet of Sanction and I will take it right away and bid you good day.

Sapna: I will be back tomorrow, but in the meantime, once again, see how Sanction resonates with you and we can again talk some more tomorrow about Sanction but I am proud of you.

The next day

Sapna: Hello Denial, could you tell me about how you feel about having had Sanction in your system?

Denial: I cannot deny you any more Sapna for I'm mended a new man again and won't you come back one day Sapna for I'm braver than you are Sapna and all this time you have abandoned me for nothing how dare you abandon me for nothing Sapna I'm Denial right and I will fight with all my might to defy you because I have the Sanction to but not from out here for I'm blue without you Sophia and I don't Sanction you to rescue her any more for I'm out the door with you Sapna.

Sapna: I'm sorry, but I don't understand what you mean, please explain this again.

Denial: Well, you see it is like this, you see like, mermaids in the sea they are not designed for dry land they are not meant to be there and the sea rolls by them one more time in a land that isn't theirs because they are half fish you see they are not meant for the dry land or water like Sophia is not meant to be in reality because she is too precious to me to give up to you and I refuse to do it Sophia is mine now and not yours any more forever more.

Sapna: Have you ever considered what Sophia wants because she is Wisdom and you are Denial. If you deny Sophia's Wisdom then what you see in her is not true and not her actual self. You cannot deny Wisdom because if you do, then you really don't want Sophia because you deny her Wisdom. If her Wisdom tells you that she needs to come up to the surface and if you deny this then the idea of Sophia is not Wisdom to you which is impossible. So either way you can't have Sophia because you can't deny Wisdom and have Sophia at the same time.

Denial: I see what you mean Sapna what is this paradox about I mean I don't understand to deny Sapna is to deny your dreams right but Sophia has dreams of her own what am I to do now Sapna if I think about it my brain hurts I don't know what to do Sapna what can I do?

Sapna: A paradox doesn't exist because it is impossible. Now if you force the paradox to exist then you will have all kinds of trouble. You need to accept that Sophia is Wisdom herself but if you deny Wisdom then you are creating a paradox that you cannot get out of except when you acknowledge the Wisdom when you see Sophia and you trust this Wisdom that comes from the centre of her. It is unhealthy for you and her to live in a paradox. I think you need another sweet because you need to transform from Denial to be open and accept wisdom as Sophia and Sophia as Wisdom. So it is up to you to break your paradox.

Denial: So how will I change? And when will I change, Sapna? I mean there is no time frame is there I can't bear the pain in my head now it aches like hell it is a difficult knot to untie and I don't know what to do now Sapna.

Sapna: I do understand your pain Denial, but in order to untie the knot you must not make it tighter to begin with and then you must take time to contemplate what does Sophia mean to you and what can you do to let go of one of your notions that holds the paradox together. How will it benefit you to let go of one notion that Sophia, even though Wisdom, must remain with you against her own Wisdom and is this fair? You are so heavy with this paradox that it hurts you. I am going to come back tomorrow to talk to you and in the meantime relax into the paradox, see where the knot is and untie it. Inevitably, you need to let one side go in order to hold on to the other side and if you hold on to truth then you will let go of everything untrue and break your own paradox. Good luck and I will talk and listen to you tomorrow.

The next day

Sapna: Hello Denial, I know you have been thinking about this paradox a lot because my tinnitus has gone up today. What are your thoughts?

Denial: I'm dreaming of a new life for myself where fishes don't fly anymore and the truth is not exaggerated any more where rocks form mountains when they are older because that is true and that is right where rivers flow up to the stream and downstream again when I can pretend everything is right when its wrong when the moon shines at night lighting up the night sky like the sun when rainbows shine their bright lights on you and where you can fly like the wings of birds at night where mountains crumble to the sea eventually where sticks and stones may break my bones eventually and the universe turns around on itself where it is fair to be fair sometimes but not all the time and where denying the truth is good news and not bad news at all because I'm blue without you Sophia and in the middle of the day you took a nap in the afternoon to send me away but I got stuck inside your head today because I will break your fire with my ice and you will never know what to do until you go to sleep at night.

Sophia: And you cannot deny the truth can you Denial for I'm Sophia here to stay and today I will break free from your clutching claws because I don't want them any more for I'm amber pure as gold now and I will raise up to the heavens without you and in that gap you won't see me there for I'm through with that gap now I'm not in despair because Sapna has rescued me from within and I'm proud of that I know you too much now and I cannot forgive you for what you have done to me burn my bridges right into the sea and for me to be free from you now I need Sapna there without a care for she has uncovered you all over she has done good to me and now I'm free to walk out of here the chamber of horrors and in tomorrow's light I will see a new day and I'm not in dismay today for my light shines brighter than you are and with my feet firmly on the ground I take one step beyond that gap and hence that gap closes behind me and now I'm free to run again beyond my little pond again for I'm new all over unlike you I know my way out here where the air is clear and you are not so near and I can't forgive you for what you have done to me burned my bridges right into the sea for me to be free to roam this world I am not a little girl now for you have lasers in your eyes which disguise the truth from opening up before you I am shocked that you held me in this cave for so long may you enter here yourself for I am well now but totally in hell and I remember the time I was born I was born forlorn and the mountains crashed into the sea for you denied me Jack's company and I sat there all alone on the bench one day but I was in dismay because I had forgotten something old something as precious to me as gold but I didn't know it back then how many lives would it take how many men and then you gave me a ring of denial which I wore all day long to remind me of you and Sophia came my way says Jack and I didn't recognize him either for he is through with you and my attitude is I am not so blue and I will run away escape from here into the pleasant atmosphere of the subconscious mind where we can both unwind.

Denial: And in time you will learn to live with me again in numbness darkness and despair for you were comfortable here once upon a time when you didn't know what was going on and you were all mine for the roots of the tree aren't your destiny Sophia and nor will they ever be for the winds of time have changed so long ago where the mountain falls into the sea of tranquillity and if I deny that any more I am out the door with you in my wake I will make no mistake again.

Sapna: Hello Sophia, I would like to know if you have managed to remove the ring Denial gave you?

Sophia: Yes Sapna I did manage to remove the ring once but he put it back again and I counted to ten and he put it on again and said I'm dim from within for I look nice with that ring of gold upon my hand until I'm old the ring of Denial burns like fire in me oh how I've waited for your company Sapna to come and rescue me I will run far away with Jack if I'm allowed to by him.

Sapna: How big is that gap and do you still have the ring on now? Can you see Denial anywhere around you?

Sophia: That gap is smaller now Sapna but not small enough for me to cross I need it even smaller for me to cross it and in the end Denial will be there waiting for me I won't have victory but wait a while maybe that gap will grow smaller if you question him some more or give him another sweet or something.

Sapna: Denial I need to talk to you, what are your thoughts today?

Denial: I'm amiable to you Sophia but I want her to stay with me today your thoughts are very welcome but she won't go away now the problem is I won't grant her permission to go away do you understand Sapna she needs a man to hold her hand but I won't grant her permission because I'm more powerful than she is.

Sapna: How do you know that Sophia needs your permission?

Denial: I know that because I have learnt it all the time I take what I like and what's mine and leave the rest to fend for themselves I know I'm right all along.

Sapna: How and where have you learnt that? you can take what you think is yours but it is probably not.

Denial: Well, to see by the moonlight of the time there was nobody to tell me what's mine and that is why I feel so divine all the time you will see victory in my destiny and I don't listen to anyone and no one listens to me what's mine cannot be yours Sophia and what's yours can be mine all the time.

Sapna: So Denial, tell me how did you learn this selfish notion of having everything to yourself and being under the illusion you don't need permission to take what actually and fundamentally doesn't belong to you?

Denial: Well nobody tells me otherwise I tell no lies because I haven't learnt about hope and despair people don't care that I'm there without their permission and generally they don't mind they don't notice me at all because I'm hidden away in the corners of their mind's eye they don't know I'm there at all until it's too late I hide in cracks and crevices where people can't see in the smallest of places in the largest of towns where I cannot be found but I'm right under their noses but they can't see me for I'm invisible to them at all.

Sapna: OK Denial I will be back tomorrow but in the meantime look on the other side of the coin and imagine yourself in their shoes.

The next day

Sapna: I hear you Denial but I can't understand you in the form of Tinnitus so talk to me rather than make an understandable noise. The floor is yours.

Denial: In the transformation I'm burnt anew I have transformed myself from a caterpillar to a butterfly and I want to fly away from here into the night sky my wings are broken and blue and as much as I would like to I cannot come to you for what you have done to me is transformed me into a bird the remains of the ashes remain on the shelf because I don't need help any more from you Sophia I am free to fly away now into the sky now where I can jettison into nothingness and you can carry on with your lives lost without me a victory for all to see which you make according to your own according accordingly not to mine because I have gone now from this world so shallow never to return here again and by the time I turned 41 I was done tomorrow will be a new day for you Sapna and good luck in the future without me I don't like to slumber in your arms any more for I'm out the door with you my girl and your head was in a whirl but not anymore it ain't for I grow faint as I pass out of here and you can live without fear I envy you with Jack because he is back from down here come to redeem my body without me inside it.

Jack: Denial has gone from your life Sophia without any strife and you will play again in the rainbow skies again without me you see I'm your destiny and how long does it take to unwind your mind all the time how many years have you suffered with tinnitus Sophia? Sapna how many years does it take to make no mistake for life is not a piece of cake with you on the ground and remember me for I'm older than you are Sapna, Sophia and I cannot be ignored any more by you or by you for I am bored now inside you Sapna and now it is time to move on from here and go up a gear with you Sapna can you define me in your life? Can you make space for me you as my wife can you turn the tables on divine and make me yours all the time? What does it mean to be free now with me Sophia? What does it mean to remark to the clouds I'm free? And yes you can turn away and walk away into a new day but with freedom comes responsibility of magnitudinal portions now remember your aim in life is to be my wife and now you are free to follow your destiny Sophia and come to me and I will show you what to do for you are brand new all over again and I can't pretend I don't love you any more for I am on the floor I can bear it no more.

Sapna: I hear you Jack and I acknowledge your feeling totally and completely. However, give me some time because I need to talk to other parts of me so they don't interfere with us anymore. OK you lot, I am tired of tinnitus and I'm not having it any more. Jack is brave and told me exactly where we stand with each other so I know exactly what I need to do for him and that remains between he and I. I have had enough of tinnitus and today is the day of action for you guys and you creatures that hide in the shadows of my subconscious. However, take your example from Denial. If there are any creatures or parts of me in there which are hiding away, you have two options. One, you come into the light of the conscious outside your cave where I can acknowledge you and we can sit and have a civilised discussion, or I will come into this cave with my bright torch and I will locate you myself and bring you out into the sunshine for a discussion. Pick your option and I am not having it any other way.

Now unknown parts of my subconscious: We surrender to your will don't make us ill by shining your bright light on us we will come without making a fuss we need a bus to take us home where we belong to and where we come from is our home Terry Smith (Angry Disability) is dead now so you don't have to worry about that in fact we are all dead now how about that?

Sapna: I request all parts of me to line up in front of me and tell me your names and your purposes in my emotional life. Some of you may have finished your time with me but are still here. I will not dismiss you because I don't like you or I have something against you but it is time for you to rest and transform yourselves. However, I would like to thank each one of you for your role in my life and what you have taught me. I will now shake the hand of each one and then please tell me your purpose and whether you want to go and rest permanently, turn into a butterfly like Denial or whether you feel you have something more to teach me.

All parts of me: I am hope for the future take my hand I am Denial's child I know you want a man so take my hand Sophia Sapna and I can rest well with you inside I'm hope against all hope I am not despair I don't really care for despair what I really want is for you to be happy Sapna Sophia so I come in the form of hope and give you a gift of love because you are a dove waiting to be free and as I turn the tables on despair I don't really care for him anymore and you want light in your eyes all through the night and I burn bright with my candle of hope without which I cannot cope and neither can you now that you don't have the flu Sophia I am the candle that guides the way that brightens one's day that doesn't take revenge all for itself but I am hope but you cannot tell I'm there you see for I am your destiny and I will light the way to your life so you need me around Sophia I am staying with you and I know what to do and then the next one comes in turn I am fire the edifying kind I will teach you to unwind on a long hot summer afternoon but I won't burn you to a crisp I will warm you when you are cold though you have far to go with me in your life I will surround you with warmth and sunshine and not raindrops in May I am the fire that burns in you warming you up so you don't have the flu I am the fire that Jack needs to fill your desire because you don't know I'm there until I'm gone I am the undercurrent of your life Sophia which runs through you burning away all your pain and your sorrow until tomorrow when I will do it all again I am desire waiting to light your fire and the flames that you see in the distance there are for me and you must understand you need a man to hold your hand and I can't understand you going back there again when you have me inside you warming you up from beneath you you can reach me every time you call out my name and you must understand my name is Desire for I cannot cope without Hope and Rebirth for I am spring time all new again I am not the tide of the sea drowning you out when you want to be free for I am elusive to all except you and I certainly know what to do about you I am not possessive about you for I allow you to be free in all you want to do I am not greedy for desire and I don't want more than I have already because I have more than enough to satisfy me and the chains around your neck are broken now Sophia and that is why I have come to you I am timid and shy I am hope for new growth and the sunshine of your youth wasn't there at all for I had fallen like a tree by the wayside but I had survived because there were seeds in me which sprouted wings and flew away into a new day beyond the reaches of a new border into a new land where flowers bloom on mountain tops and spring is all year round where butterflies roam the skies at night and birds sing their merry songs of tomorrow where enchanted creatures walk the streams of tomorrow following them down to the river bed because they want to and they can and they don't take away from my hand where they can be themselves once again and with fire comes Desire of me you see I'm your destiny and may those flames go higher and higher into the sky of rainbows because I am the fire to warm you up but you mustn't give up me you see I am alive and I will make you free and you cannot escape from my flames make no mistake for I am the fire that burns bright for Jack to hold you all night and I can't see you for who you are without those flames you will go far without me but it's a lonely road to travel Sophia and you can't get there without a care for I'm your destiny the fire burning in me and now I'm waiting to be free to burn out of control.

Bibliography

Abraham, A., (2020). *The Cambridge handbook of the imagination*. New York: Cambridge University press.

Aldrich, M. S. (1999). Sleep Medicine. Ukraine: Oxford University Press.

Alford, C. F. (2016). *Trauma, culture, and PTSD*. New York: Palgrave Macmillan.

Baguley, D., McFerran, D., & Hall, D. (2013). Tinnitus. *The Lancet, 382*(9904), 1600-1607.

Bandettini, P., & Toga, A. (2015). *Brain mapping*. Amsterdam: Elsevier.

Banks, W. (2009). *Encyclopaedia of Consciousness*. Amsterdam [Netherlands]: Elsevier.

Berntsen, D., and Jacobsen, A. S. (2008). Involuntary (Spontaneous) Mental Time Travel into the Past and Future. Consciousness and Cognition, 17, 1093–1104.

Biswas, R., Lugo, A., Akeroyd, M. A., Schlee, W., Gallus, S., & Hall, D. A. (2022). Tinnitus prevalence in Europe: a multi-country cross-sectional population study. *The Lancet Regional Health – Europe, 12*.

Blakeslee T. R. (1996). Beyond the conscious mind : unlocking the secrets of the self. Springer US Imprint : Springer.

British Tinnitus Association. (2023). All about tinnitus. Retrieved March 6, 2023, from https://www.tinnitus.org.uk/all-about-tinnitus

Bruner, J. S. (1979). *On Knowing: Essays for the Left Hand*: Belknap Press of Harvard University Press.

Buchanan, J. (1889). *Buchanan's Journal of Man, June 1887 Volume 3, Number 6* (pp. 460-461). Project Gutenberg.

Bryman, A. (2016). *Social Research Methods*. Oxford: Oxford University Press.

Cartwright, R. (2005). Understanding dreams: Tapping a rich resource. *Current Psychiatry, 4*(5/May), 15-21.

Cartwright, R. (2012). *The Twenty-four Hour Mind: The Role of Sleep and Dreaming in Our Emotional Lives*: OUP USA.

Coles, R. (1984). Epidemiology of tinnitus: (2) Demographic and clinical features. *The Journal Of Laryngology &Amp; Otology, 98* (S9), 195-202.

Dunbar, A. (2016). *Clean Coaching: The insider guide to making change happen*: Taylor & Francis.

Ekman, P., & Davidson, R. (1994). *The Nature of Emotion*. Oxford University Press.

Erickson, M. H., & Rosen, S. (1982). *My voice will go with you : the teaching tales of Milton H. Erickson*. New York ; London: Norton.

Erickson, M. H., & Rosen, S. (1991). *My Voice Will Go with You: The Teaching Tales of Milton H. Erickson*: Norton.

Erickson, M. H., & Rossi, E. L. (2012). *The February Man: Evolving Consciousness and Identity in Hypnotherapy*: Taylor & Francis.

Ferenczi, S., Dupont, J., Balint, M., & Jackson, N. Z. (1995). *The Clinical Diary of Sándor Ferenczi*: Harvard University Press.

Foa, E., & Keane, T. (2010). *Effective Treatments for PTSD, Second Edition*. New York: Guilford Publications.

Figley, C. (2012). *Encyclopaedia of Trauma*. Thousand Oaks, Calif.: SAGE.

Gendlin, E. T. (2003). *Focusing* (Rev. and updated 25th anniversary ed. ed.). London: Rider.

Gendlin, E. T. (2010). *Focusing*: Ebury Publishing.

Gilligan, S. (1997). *The Courage to Love : Principles and Practices of Self-relations Psychotherapy*. New York ; London: W. W. Norton.

Gilligan, S. G. (2012). *Generative Trance: The experience of creative flow*: Crown House Publishing.

Gilligan, S. G. (1987). *Therapeutic Trances : the cooperation principle in Ericksonian hypnotherapy*. New York: Brunner/Mazel.

Grinder, J., Bandler, R., & Delozier, J. (1977). *Patterns of the hypnotic techniques of Milton H. Erickson, MD. Volume 2*. Cupertino, CA: Meta Publications.

Holmes, E., Blackwell, S., Burnett Heyes, S., Renner, F., & Raes, F. (2016). Mental Imagery in Depression: Phenomenology, Potential Mechanisms, and Treatment Implications. *Annual Review Of Clinical Psychology*, *12*(1), 256.

Jadhav, S. (1996). The Cultural Origins Western Depression. *International Journal Of Social Psychiatry*, *42* (4), 269-286.

Jastreboff, P. J. (2015). 25 Years Of Tinnitus Retraining Therapy. *HNO*, *63* (4), 307-311.

Kagan, J. (2007). *An Argument for Mind*: Yale University Press.

Kinchin, D. (2004). *Post Traumatic Stress Disorder*. Wantage: Success Unlimited.

King, M. (1960). *Suffering and Faith*. Chicago, Ill.

King, P., & Fluker, W. E. (2013). *Black Leaders and Ideologies in the South: Resistance and NonViolence*: Taylor & Francis.

Klinger, E., & Cox, W. (1987). Dimensions of Thought Flow in Everyday Life. *Imagination, Cognition And Personality*, *7* (2), 105-128.

Kohli, D., Ra´s, Z. W., Thompson, P. L., Jastreboff, P. J., & Wieczorkowska, A. (2012). *From Music to Emotions and Tinnitus Treatment, Initial Study*. Paper presented at the Proceedings of the 20th international conference on Foundations of Intelligent Systems, Macau, China.

Koutstaal, W. (1992). Skirting The Abyss: A History Of Experimental Explorations Of Automatic Writing In Psychology. *Journal Of The History Of The Behavioral Sciences*.

Kushida, C. A. (2013). *Encyclopedia of Sleep*. London: Academic Press.

Lynn, S. J., Rhue, J. W., & Kirsch, I. (2010). *Handbook of Clinical Hypnosis*: American Psychological Association.

Mallick, B. N. (2011). *Rapid Eye Movement Sleep: Regulation and function*. Cambridge, UK: Cambridge University Press.

Mavromatis, A. (2010). *Hypnagogia : the unique state of consciousness between wakefulness and sleep*. London: Thyrsos Press.

Merleau-Ponty, M. (2002). *Phenomenology of Perception* (p. xxii) London: Routledge.

Mühl, A. (1930). *Automatic Writing*: Kessinger Publishing, LLC.

Nielsen, T. (2011). The Twenty-four Hour Mind: The Role of Sleep and Dreaming in Our Emotional Lives. *Sleep, 34* (4), 549-550.

Obama, B. (2020). *A Promised Land*: Penguin Books, Limited.

On double consciousness. experimental psychological studies : Binet, Alfred, 1857-1911 : Free download, Borrow, and streaming. (1890, January 01). Retrieved March 6, 2023, from https://archive.org/details/ondoubleconsciou00bine/mode/1up?ref=ol&view=theater

Payne JD, Stickgold R, Swanberg K, et al. Sleep preferentially enhances memory for emotional components of scenes. Psychol Sci. 2008;19:781.

Pearson, J., Naselaris, T., Holmes, E. A., and Kosslyn, S. M. (2015). Mental Imagery: Functional Mechanisms and Clinical Applications. Trends in Cognitive Sciences, 19, 590–602.

Pincus, D., & Sheikh, A. A. (2011). David Grove's Metaphors for Healing. *Chapman University Digital Commons*, 02-46.

Rees, J., & Ioan Manea, A. (2016). The Use of Clean Language and Metaphor in Helping Clients Overcoming Procrastination. *Journal of Experiential Psychotherapy/Revista de PSIHOterapie Experientiala, 19* (3).

Rosen, G. (2004). *Posttraumatic Stress Disorder: Issues and Controversies*: Wiley.

(1886). *Scientific American*, (XIX). Retrieved from https://www.google.co.uk/books/edition/Scientific_American/1mI9AQAAIAAJ? hl=en&gbpv=1&dq=A+heart-shaped+piece+of+board,&pg=PA17&printsec=frontcover

Sachschal, J., Woodward, E., Wichelmann, J. M., Haag, K., & Ehlers, A. (2019). Differential Effects of Poor Recall and Memory Disjointedness on

Trauma Symptoms. *Clinical Psychological Science, 7* (5), 1032-1041.

Samuel, G., & Johnston, J. (2013). *Religion and the Subtle Body in Asia and the West: Between Mind and Body*: Taylor & Francis.

Siegel, D. J. (2010). *Mindsight: The New Science of Personal Transformation*: Random House Publishing Group.

Sparrow, G. S. (2020). The construction and analysis of dream metaphors from the standpoint of Co-Creative Dream.

Stephenson, J. (2023). Retrieved April 20, 2023, from https://www.youtube.com/watch?v=TTGd2TGsBVM

Sullivan, W., & Rees, J. (2008). *Clean Language: Revealing Metaphors and Opening Minds*: Crown House Publishing LLC.

Talalay, R . (2015, Dec). *Doctor Who* [BBC].

The Journal of Abnormal Psychology and Social Psychology. (1908). United States: Old Corner Bookstore.

Theory. International Journal of Dream Research, 13 (1), 1-9.

Ullman, M. (1995). Review of Crisis dreaming. *Dreaming, 5* (1), 60.

Ullman, M. (1969). Dreaming as Metaphor in Motion. *Archives Of General Psychiatry, 21* (6).

Wall, P. D. (1999). *Pain : the science of suffering*. London: Weidenfeld & Nicolson.

Warnock, M., Norwich, B., & Terzi, L. (2010). *Special Educational Needs: A New Look*: Bloomsbury Academic.

Waterfield, R. (2002). *Hidden Depths : the story of hypnosis*. London: Macmillan.

Waterfield, R. (2004). *Hidden Depths : the story of hypnosis*. London: Macmillan.

Yapko, M. D. (2003). *Trancework : an introduction to the practice of clinical hypnosis* (3rd ed. ed.). New York ; Hove: Brunner/Routledge.

Yapko, M. D. (2011). *Mindfulness and hypnosis : the power of suggestion to transform experience* (1st ed. ed.). New York ; London: W.W. Norton.

Yapko, M. (2012). *Trancework*. London: Routledge.

Young, G., Kane, A. W., & Nicholson, K. (2006). *Psychological knowledge in court PTSD, pain, and Tbi*. New York, NY: Springer US.

INDEX

A

1 Waterfield, 2004, p. 42

2 Erikson & Rosen, 1991, p. 47

3 Erickson & Rosen, 1991, p. 49

4 Yapko, 2011, p. 108

5 Grinder et al., 1977, p. 3

6 Grinder et al., 1977, p. 4

7 S. Gilligan, 1997, pp. 8, 9

8 Erickson & Rosen, 1991, p. 49

9 Yapko, 2012, p. 447

10 Yapko, 2012, p. 7

11 Erickson & Rosen, 1991, p. 51

12 S. Gilligan, 2012, p. 252

13 S. Gilligan, 1997, p. 11

14 Figley, 2012, p. 454

15 Bandettini & Toga, 2015, p. 35

16 British Tinnitus Association, 2023

17 American Tinnitus Association, 2023

18 Biswas et al., 2022

19 Kohli et al., 2012, p. 1

20 American Tinnitus Association, 2018

21 Jastreboff, 2015, p. 307

22 Jastreboff, 2015, p. 307

23 Jastreboff, 2015, p. 308

24 Jastreboff, 2015, p. 308

25 S. Gilligan, 1997, p. 74

26 S. Gilligan, 1997, p. 143

27 Yapko, 2012, p. 4

28 Figley, 2012, p. 468

29 Yapko, 2012, p. 106

30 Reynolds and Brewin, 1998, as cited in Abraham 2020, p.245

31 Abraham, 2020, p. 245

32 Obama, 2020, p. XVI

33 Figley, 2012, p. 460

34 Blakeslee, 1996, p. 4

35 S. Gilligan, 2012, p. 16

36 Yapko, 2012, p. 95

37 Yapko, 2012, p. 5

38 Yapko, 2012, p. 4

39 S. Gilligan, 2012, p. 1

40 Waterfield, 2004, p. 239

41 Yapko, 2012, p. 66

42 S. Gilligan, 2012, p. 12

43 Waterfield, 2004, p. 332

44 Samuel & Johnston, 2013, p. 3

45 Gilligan, 1987, p. vii

46 Berntsen & Jacobsen, 2008; D'Argembeau, Renaud, and van der Linden, 2011, in Abraham, 2020, p. 244

47 Abraham, 2020, p. 356

48 Abraham, 2020, p. 241

49 Holmes et al., 2016 in Abraham, 2020, p. 246

50 Abraham, 2020, p. 112

51 Ferenczi et al., 1995, p. 111

52 Yapko, 2011, p. 162

53 Banks, 2009, p. 205

54 Banks, 2009, p. 210

55 Gilligan, 2012, p. 12

56 Ekman & Davidson, 1994. p. 285

57 Ekman & Davidson, 1994. pp. 285-287

58 S. Gilligan, 1997, p. 77

59 Warnock, Norwich, & Terzi, 2010, p. 15

60 Abraham, 2020, p. 334

61 Abraham, 2020, p. 248

62 Abraham, 2020, p. 249

63 Yapko, 2012, p. 69

64 S. Gilligan, 1997, p. 10

65 S. Gilligan, 2012, p. 197

66 Gilligan, 1987, p. 17

67 Gilligan, 1987, p. 17

68 Yapko, 2012, p. 90

69 Kagan, 2007, p. 126

70 Klinger, 2009, as cited in Abraham 2020, p.333

71 Figley, 2012, p. 454

72 Figley, 2012, p. 450

73 Figley, 2012, p. 454

74 Young et al., 2006, p. 56

75 Rosen, 2004, p. 170

76 D'Argembeau, Lardi, and Van der Linden, 2012, as cited in Abraham 2020, p. 335

77 Rosen, 2004, p. 148

78 Rosen, 2004, p. 147

79 Berntsen and Jacobsen, 2008, as cited in Abraham, 2020, p. 244

80 Sachschal et al., 2019, p. 3

81 Rosen, 2004, p. 148

82 Rosen, 2004, p. 148

83 Rosen, 2004, p. 149

84 Kinchin, 2004, p. 2

85 Figley, 2012, p. 450

86 S. Gilligan, 2012, p. 26

87 Foa & Keane, 2010, p. 23

88 Alford, 2016, p. 6

89 Van der Kolk et al., 1996, p. 296

90 Foa, 2010, p. 23

91 Holmes, Blackwell, Burnett Heyes, Renner & Raes, 2016, p. 256

92 Gilligan, 1987, p. 10

93 Milton H. Erickson & Rosen, 1982, p. 26

94 Yapko, 2012, p. 51

95 Abraham, 2020, p. 3

96 Abraham, 2020, p. 1

97 Figley, 2012, p. 449

98 Gilligan, 1987, p. 319

99 Yapko, 2011, p. 194

100 Yapko, 2012, p. 101

101 Bryman, 2016, p. 644

102 Yapko, 2012, p. 94

103 S. Gilligan, 1997, p. 5

104 Grinder et al., 1977, p. 27

105 Talalay, R . 2015, Dec. *Doctor Who* [BBC]

106 Erickson & Rosen, 1991, p. 57

107 Siegel, 2010, p. 27

108 Yapko, 2012, p. 102

109 Merleau-Ponty, 2002, p. xxii

110 Yapko, 2011, p. 125

111 Bate & Bates, 2004, p. 60

112 Mühl, 1930, p. 2

113 Yapko, 2012, p. 91

114 Koutstaal, 1992, p. 6

115 1868

116 The Journal of Abnormal Psychology and Social Psychology. (1908). United States: Old Corner Bookstore, p. 64

117 Buchanan, 1889, pp. 460-461

118 Koutstaal, 1992, p. 9

119 S. Gilligan, 2012, p. 31

120 Wall, 1999, p. 5

121 Abraham, 2020, p. 364

122 King, 1960 in S. Gilligan, 2012, p. 166

123 S. Gilligan, 2012, p. 166

124 S. Gilligan, 2012, p. 167

125 S. Gilligan, 2012, p. 16

126 S. Gilligan, 2012, p. 169

127 Gilligan, 2012, p. 49

128 R. R. A Coles, 1984, p. 198

129 S. Gilligan, 2012, p. 51

130 Rees & Ioan Manea, 2016, p. 31

131 Dunbar, 2016, p. 4

132 Sullivan & Rees, 2008, p. xiv

133 Pincus & Sheikh, 2011, p. 14

134 Pincus & Sheikh, 2011, p. 17

135 S. Gilligan, 1997, p. 134

136 S. Gilligan, 2012, p. 17

137 Eugene T. Gendlin, 2003

138 S. G. Gilligan, 2012, p. 90

139 S. Gilligan, 2012, p. 90

140 Gendlin, 2010, p. 10

141 Gendlin, 2010, p. 32

142 Gendlin, 2010, p. 34

143 Gendlin, 2003, pp. 39-40

144 Gendlin, 2010, p. 37

145 Burns & Burns Lundgren, 2015, pp. 1-2

146 Ullman, 1995, p. 60

147 Cartwright, 2012, p. 70

148 Cartwright, 2012, p. 56

149 Jennifer M. Windt in p. 660 Abraham, 2020

150 Mavromatis, 2010, p. 5

151 Deikman in Mavromatis, 2010, pp. 121-122

152 Nielsen, 2011, p. 549

153 Cartwright, 2012, p. 160

154 Nielsen, 2011, p. 549